BRITISH MUS

INSECTS
INSTRUCTIONS FOR COLLECTORS No 4a

Fifth Edition (Completely Revised)
Trustees of the British Museum (Natural History)
London 1974

First printed	.	.	.	1940
Second edition	.	.	.	1949
Third edition	.	.	.	1954
Fourth edition	.	.	.	1963
Fifth Edition (Completely revised) 1974				

© Trustees of the British Museum (Natural History) 1974

Publication number 705   ISBN 0 565 05705 7

Printed in England by Staples Printers Limited at The George Press, Kettering
Northamptonshire

PREFACE

The first edition of this work was compiled by Dr John Smart and published in 1940; new editions were printed from time to time, the fourth appearing in 1963. It has long been clear that a complete revision was needed to take account of the many new techniques and advances that have been introduced in recent years.

Accordingly, Messrs B H Cogan and K G V Smith, of the Department of Entomology, were asked to produce an entirely rewritten text, drawing both on their own experience in the field and also on that of their colleagues. The resulting handbook gives a new and up-to-date account of modern methods of insect collecting, packing and transport which it is hoped will be of use to collectors, especially those whose insects are destined to come to the Museum. **However, it cannot be too strongly emphasized that indiscriminate collecting especially of rare species, particularly butterflies, should not be undertaken.** Further information on this point can be found in the section on butterflies (p. 98).

As in previous editions a part of the book deals with general methods and descriptions of apparatus and their use. A separate part deals with insects belonging to each Order to help not only in their recognition but also in the specialized methods normally employed in their collection. Particular attention is paid to the dangers to man inherent in the use of some of the killing agents and also to the care needed when collecting in countries – mainly tropical – where water-borne and other diseases are rife.

It is, however, not enough just to collect; the condition of the specimens collected is of prime importance. Indeed, from the point of view of the Museum, everything depends upon the condition in which the specimens arrive; it is as disappointing to the staff of the Museum as it must be to the collector when material, obtained perhaps with much difficulty, proves on receipt to be quite useless simply because certain elementary precautions have not been taken, or essential information has been omitted. With this in mind, the staff of the Department of Entomology are always willing to advise collectors who wish to place some or all of their captures in the Museum.

British Museum (Natural History)   **Paul Freeman**

20 March 1973   **Keeper of Entomology**

CONTENTS

CONTENTS

INTRODUCTION

Collections of animals are maintained in museums so that examples of as many species as possible may be available for reference and study. There are many reasons for requiring such collections and many ways of studying the individual specimens or species, but the prime reason in the larger museums is to enable animals to be identified or described and to give them standard Latin names. The work of the staff of such a museum is largely the description and preparation of revisions, monographs and catalogues of the species, the study of their relationships and the maintenance of the reference collection of the animals themselves. Once an animal bears a name, information on its biology, distribution and medical or economic importance can be collated.

The number of species of insects is very great and at present about 750 000 are known, representing about three-quarters of the total number of animal species. It is thought that the final number will be much higher, certainly twice as many and possibly more. Insects lend themselves to collecting, many being colourful, attractive and easily caught. The majority can be readily preserved dry, usually with a pin through the thorax, and collections can thus be built up in a reasonably simple way. The British Museum (Natural History) insect collections now contain an estimated 17 500 000 specimens with a further 250 000 being added each year, but, even so, hardly more than half of the known species are represented, though of course many await description in the accession material.

This handbook is intended primarily for those wishing to collect insects for the British Museum (Natural History), South Kensington, London, and the methods described are those that the Museum staff find best to obtain suitable specimens for the National Collection. It is, however, hoped that others may find the instructions useful should they wish to build up a study collection for their own use.

GENERAL CONSIDERATIONS

Modern systematic study of any group of animals requires as large a series of specimens as is possible, or practical; they must be well preserved and in good condition. Such study enables the specialist to examine minute variations and perhaps to correlate them with region or habitat and thus to improve knowledge of specific and racial differences. Collectors should, therefore, not be content with small samples even of species appearing to be abundant, but should collect good series from as many different places as possible. It is not at all unusual for insects that are rare in collections to appear quite commonly in restricted localities for short emergence periods.

The scientific staff of the Museum are always willing to advise on groups of insects particularly needed from any given area, and they will give any other assistance in their power. It is recommended that collectors get in touch with the Department of Entomology for advice and discussion before they set out.

In general, the Museum wants insects of some kind from almost everywhere but it is impossible to state these requirements here in any detail; they can only be explained by personal consultation. As an example, the Museum collection of butterflies, an attractive group of showy insects, contains representatives of over 90 per cent. of the described species. Hence a collector wishing to concentrate on these insects would need to be advised on which types are still needed—in this case it would be the smaller, less conspicuous species. On the other hand the Museum collections of flies and parasitic Hymenoptera contain no more than 33 per cent. of the described species and useful collections of these can be made almost anywhere, especially among the smaller species. It is worth mentioning that in the British fauna of some 21 000 species of insect, new species are still to be found among the lesser-known groups.

2

INSECTS AND THE ARTHROPODA

Insects form the largest Class of the group or Phylum of invertebrate animals called the Arthropoda. This Phylum contains at least 85 per cent. of all known species of animals and includes such familiar forms as crabs, shrimps, spiders and centipedes, as well as the true insects (Insecta).

The Arthropoda have the body divided into separate rings or segments each of which may bear jointed limbs. As in other Invertebrata, there is no extensive internal skeleton to give support to the body and attachments for the muscles. Instead, these functions are performed mainly by the thickening and hardening of the integument to form an exoskeleton. In insects the outer covering or cuticle contains a fibrous nitrogenous polysaccharide called chitin, hardened where necessary by the addition of protein to form sclerotin which is in effect a cross-linked plastic. Hardened areas of exoskeleton are linked by flexible areas between segments to allow movement.

Adult insects possess the following characteristics:

1 The body is divided into three regions: head, thorax and abdomen;

2 The head carries one pair of antennae only, one pair of mandibles and two pairs of maxillae, the second pair fused medially to form the labium;

3 The thorax carries three pairs of walking legs and usually one or two pairs of wings;

4 The abdomen has no walking appendages;

5 Respiration is by means of branching air tubes or tracheae opening through spiracles along the sides of the body.

Larvae of the more advanced insects may be profoundly different from the adults, and in particular, structures such as wings, legs, compound eyes, mouthparts and external genitalia may be considerably modified or entirely absent.

The other main groups of Arthropoda, none of which possess wings, can be distinguished from the Insecta as follows:

3

1 *Crustacea* (crabs, shrimps, woodlice, etc) have two pairs of antennae and at least five pairs of legs; when the body segments are grouped, they are arranged in two regions only; respiration is never by tracheae.

2 *Arachnida* (spiders, mites, scorpions, etc) have no antennae and four pairs of legs; the body segments are either grouped in two regions or are fused into an unsegmented whole; respiration is sometimes by tracheae.

3 *Diplopoda* (millipedes) have a single pair of antennae; the body trunk is not differentiated into thorax and abdomen; each apparent segment bears two pairs of legs and spiracles; respiration is by tracheae.

4 *Chilopoda* (centipedes) resemble Diplopoda superficially but each segment is a true segment carrying only a single pair of legs and spiracles. The first pair of legs is modified into poison claws.

Insects are the most successful and abundant living animals and have colonised practically all terrestrial and freshwater ecological niches; a small number have succeeded in adapting themselves to life below high tide mark and a very few to the surface of the open sea. They are one of Man's main competitors and many species impinge directly upon his activities. Some, of which the locusts are prime examples, can devastate his crops, others such as mosquitoes are active transmitters of various diseases such as malaria.

DEVELOPMENT AND LIFE HISTORY OF INSECTS

Most insects start life as eggs laid by adult females following mating with adult males. Occasionally the eggs hatch before being laid, so that the female appears to lay larvae. Other insects are able to lay unfertilized eggs that hatch normally (parthenogenesis) and in still other, much rarer cases, immature forms may reproduce (paedogenesis). On hatching, young insects may resemble the adults in general features, eg young cockroaches, or they may be very different, eg caterpillars and fly maggots. Young insects, with the possible exception of mayflies, never have functional wings.

4

As in the adult, the young insect is covered by a chitinous cuticle, with hardened parts and plates. The softer parts are provided with a loosely fitting and folded superficial epicuticle which allows room for growth. The more rigid parts such as mandibles and legs have no room for growth after their initial hardening. When the limit set by the extensibility of the epicuticle and the size of the harder parts is reached, the inner layers of the old cuticle are dissolved from within and a new cuticle, a size larger, is laid down beneath the old one. After an appreciable thickness of new cuticle has been laid down, the old cuticle is ruptured along definite lines of weakness and the insect gently withdraws itself from the remnants of the old skin. The new skin in turn becomes extended to its limit and is eventually cast off, until, after a series of such moults or ecdyses, maturity is reached and, normally, growth ceases.

The life cycle of an insect may be divided into three distinct phases: 1 the egg; 2 the growing stage, or larva; 3 the adult or imago, when it becomes sexually mature. In the higher Orders, where the difference in form and habit between larva and adult is great (as between a maggot and a bluebottle), there is an intermediate quiescent stage, called the pupa (Fig. 1). In those Orders of insects in which the young resemble the adults in form and to some extent in habit, and in which this pupa stage is not present, the young insect is usually termed a nymph (Fig. 2). Some entomologists do not use the term nymph but refer to all as larvae. The changes of form through which an insect passes are collectively termed metamorphosis.

With a few rare exceptions, it is only in the adult stage that insects are sexually mature and capable of reproduction. With the exception of some of the very primitive insects, moulting ceases with sexual maturity. The young stages are usually voracious feeders, while the adults are more concerned with reproduction and the search for new feeding grounds for their young.

The young stages of many insects live in places quite different from those in which the adults are found. Thus, mosquito larvae are aquatic, and many fly maggots live and grow in decaying flesh and other putrid matter. Invasion of quite different habitats by the young stages has become possible with the evolution of meta-morphosis.

CLASSIFICATION

Insects are a Class of the superclass Hexapoda of the Phylum Arthropoda. They can be divided into two Subclasses according to whether the wings are considered to be primitively absent or not. The second Subclass is further divided according to the type of metamorphosis. In the classification recognized here there are 25

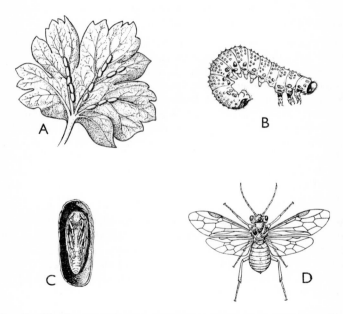

Fig. 1. The development of a Holometabolous Insect, one of the Saw-flies, *Pteronidea ribesii* (Scop.) ×2½ approx. A, Eggs on leaf; B, The larva; C, The pupa in its cocoon which has been cut open to expose the pupa; D, The adult sawfly (imago).

Orders, mostly placed in the second Subclass. Of the 4 Orders formerly included in the first Subclass the Diplura, Protura and Collembola are now widely given Class status.

SUPERCLASS HEXAPODA

Class and Order Diplura (some bristletails). (Fig. 20)

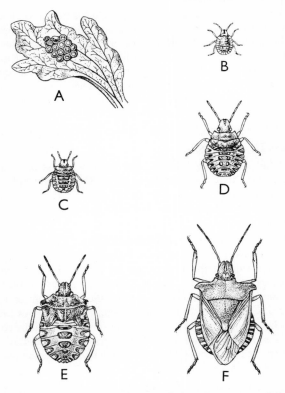

Fig. 2. The development of a Hemimetabolous Insect, one of the Bugs. *Pentatoma rufipes* (L.) ×2. A, Eggs with first instar nymphs hatching; B, Second instar (nymph); C, Third instar (nymph); D, Fourth instar (nymph); E, Fifth instar (nymph); F, Final or adult, instar (imago).

Class and Order Protura (microscopic soil insects, no common name) (Fig. 20)

Class and Order Collembola (springtails). (Fig. 20)

Subclass I. Apterygota

The above three orders were formerly included here and along with the single insect order now included are wingless arthropods of primitive structure with virtually no metamorphosis.   The young resemble the adults in all essential features except sexual maturity and size.   They usually go through many moults and may continue moulting after reaching sexual maturity.   Their wingless condition is considered to be primitive, ie at no time in their evolutionary history have they ever possessed wings.

Order 1 Thysanura (silverfish, bristletails, firebrats) (Fig. 20).

Subclass II. Pterygota

This includes all winged insects and those wingless ones, such as lice and fleas, that are considered to be secondarily apterous, ie winged forms have occurred at some point in their evolutionary history.   Their metamorphosis is varied, but it is rarely only slight or wanting.

Division 1. Exopterygota (or Hemimetabola).   The young, usually termed nymphs, bear a close resemblance to their parents, with the wings appearing in the later stages of nymphal life as pads developing externally on the thorax (hence the name Exopterygota). There may be a change of habitat when the adult stage is assumed but there is rarely a resting stage or pupa.   The changes that take place when the nymph becomes an adult are usually sufficient to be called a partial metamorphosis.   The first two Orders are sometimes regarded as forming the infraclass Palaeoptera, the remainder forming the infraclass Neoptera.

Order 2 Ephemeroptera (mayflies)   (Fig. 21)
Order 3 Odonata (dragonflies)   (Fig. 21)
Order 4 Dictyoptera (cockroaches and mantises)   (Fig. 23)
Order 5 Isoptera (termites)   (Fig. 22)

Order 6 Plecoptera (stoneflies)   (Fig. 21)

Order 7 Grylloblattodea (small rare group, no common name)

Order 8 Dermaptera (earwigs)   (Fig. 23)

Order 9 Phasmida (stick- and leaf-insects)   (Fig. 23)

Order 10 Orthoptera (crickets and grasshoppers)   (Fig. 23)

Order 11 Embioptera (web-spinners)   (Fig. 22)

Order 12 Zoraptera (small rare group, no common name)   (Fig. 23)

Order 13 Psocoptera (psocids and book-lice)   (Fig. 22)

Order 14 Thysanoptera (thrips)   (Fig. 22)

Order 15 Phthiraptera [= Mallophaga (biting or bird-lice) and Anoplura (sucking lice)]   (Fig. 36)

Order 16 Hemiptera (plant-bugs, bed-bugs, plant lice, scale-insects, etc)   (Fig. 24)

Division 2. Endopterygota (or Holometabola). The young, termed larvae, bear little resemblance to their parents and the change to adult is complex and always includes a resting stage or pupa during which the insect does not feed and is apparently quiescent, although great internal changes are taking place. In this group the wings develop internally in the larva (hence Endopterygota) and do not become visible externally until the pupal stage. The changes that take place are said to form a complete metamorphosis.

Order 17 Neuroptera (alderflies, lacewings, ant-lions, etc)   (Fig. 25)

Order 18 Mecoptera (scorpionflies)   (Fig. 25)

Order 19 Trichoptera (caddisflies)   (Fig. 25)

Order 20 Lepidoptera (butterflies and moths)   (Figs 26, 27)

Order 21 Diptera (two-winged flies, gnats, etc)   (Fig. 30)

Order 22 Siphonaptera (fleas)   (Fig. 36)

Order 23 Hymenoptera (bees, wasps, ants, etc)   (Fig. 31)

Order 24 Coleoptera (beetles)   (Fig. 33)

Order 25 Strepsiptera (rare insect parasites, no common name)   (Fig. 36)

ZOOGEOGRAPHY AND THE DISTRIBUTION OF INSECTS

High mountain ranges, oceans and deserts provide barriers to the dispersal of terrestrial animals; insects seem to be especially affected by desert areas. The limits imposed by these factors and by climatic and other conditions, have resulted in the development of the faunas of the larger land masses upon lines so characteristic that zoologists have been able to define six main faunistic regions.

The Palaearctic Region is approximately the whole of the Old World north of a line running through the Saharan and Middle Eastern deserts and along the Himalayan chain to the China Sea by way of the Yang-tse-Kiang River. The Nearctic Region is roughly America north of Mexico. These two Regions show many points of similarity, and there are numerous species common to both; they are frequently given the comprehensive term Holarctic.

The remainder of Africa and Madagascar form the Ethiopian Region, which is now sometimes called 'Africa south of the Sahara'. The Oriental Region comprises all the tropical eastern lands and islands, except for Australia, New Guinea and certain neighbouring islands, which, together with New Zealand and the Pacific Islands, are known collectively as the Australasian Region.

The Regions are based largely on the distribution of mammals and birds and have not always been found to apply quite so convincingly to insects. They were first worked out by Sclater and adapted by A R Wallace and the map in Fig. 3 shows the Regions as defined by these workers with their major Sub-Regions.

There will seldom be any doubt as to the Region into which any given country falls except along the boundaries of the faunistic Regions. In these areas there is inevitable infiltration of elements from one Region to another and care must be taken in using faunistic keys to species. Particular places where difficulties occur are in the Middle East where the Palaearctic and Oriental Regions meet the Ethiopian; in the Himalayas, China and Japan, where Palaearctic and Oriental Regions meet; and in Mexico, where there is overlap between Nearctic and Neotropical Regions.

10

Probably one of the most confusing areas is the division between Oriental and Australasian Regions. The classical dividing line

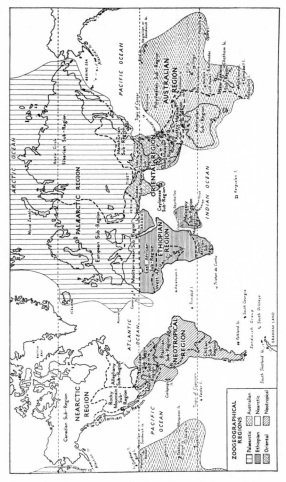

FIG. 3. Map showing zoogeographic regions of the world.

11

here is 'Wallace's Line' which runs through the Macassar and Lombok Straits and thus places Celebes and Timor, etc, in the Australasian Region.   Lee and Woodhill (1944) suggest that the dividing line is immediately west of Molucca, Ceram, Wetter and Timor, ie more to the east, but it seems that the line varies greatly from group to group within the insects.

GENERAL COLLECTING

INTRODUCTION

This section of the hand book includes all those aspects of general collecting suitable for the amassing of collections and the subsequent preservation and treatment of the material. There are, of course, a limitless number of techniques for every aspect of collecting and no two experienced collectors are likely to agree on the most satisfactory methods, equipment or conditions for any single group of insects. It is, therefore, necessary to separate the most basic of these techniques, including the use of equipment common to the collection of the majority of the insect orders, from those which will almost certainly only be applicable to special groups of insects or specific ecological or climatological conditions.

These general methods etc, are dealt with below in a strictly functional sequence, namely: collecting, killing, preserving and preparing, packing, storing and transporting.

APPARATUS AND METHODS

General collecting may be divided for convenience of description into three broad categories:

(A)   the collecting of individual specimens, in which the collector makes a conscious choice of the specimen to be taken, using forceps, tube, net or aspirator;

(B)   the collecting of numbers of specimens, at one and the same time, in which the collector searches for insects in specific habitats and uses techniques and equipment for mass collecting: eg beating trays, sweep nets, sieves and funnel extractors;

(C) the mass collecting of specimens in which the collector uses very little discrimination in respect to what he catches, but relies on traps, the latter with or without attractants, be they lights, chemical or natural baits.

The collection of individual specimens is most commonly used for large or fragile species, for particularly scarce insects, or when conditions militate against the use of the mass collecting techniques.

Special Instruments

Every entomologist should provide himself with a special set of instruments apart from the usual collecting apparatus of nets, killing jars etc. This set should contain as a minimum, the following:

blunt and fine tipped forceps,
pinning forceps for pinning small insects in the field,
camel-hair brush,
scissors, blunt and fine tipped,
setting needles, or stout bristle in holder,
lens, × 10, 15 or 20, with a lanyard.

All the above may be housed in a canvas 'roll' as sold to carry biological dissecting kits. The use of these instruments requires little amplification; the forceps and camel-hair brush enable selected specimens of a variety of sizes to be collected. The forceps require some care in their manipulation to avoid damaging specimens and are usually only used for larger insects of a terrestrial nature eg coleoptera, large running ants, and lepidopterous larvae. The camel-hair brush, for use with very small insects, should be wetted before use with the fluid in which the specimens are to be killed and stored.

In addition, the collector will require various specialised tools, these depending upon the habitat to be worked, and a variety of tubes and boxes in which to place his captures if they are not to be killed immediately.

A trowel, preferably of stainless steel, is necessary for digging among eaf litter, digging out nests of insects, small mammals or birds. A

14

strong broad-bladed knife, either with a rigid blade and sheath, or of the folding jack-knife variety, is considered indispensable by many collectors. If one is not too much of a purist such a knife may be used for a great variety of purposes – digging, bark stripping, beating etc – and dispenses with the need for a host of specialised tools.

Tubes

There are now available a very large selection of tubes, both in clear glass and in plastic or some other substitute, with rubber, cork or plastic stoppers. The choice of tube must depend on the purpose in mind. It should be remembered, however, that the greater the variety of tubes and stoppers one uses, the greater the frustration when packing the tubes into boxes for carriage, or when replacing lost stoppers in tubes, and in matching up mixed tubes and corks. Wherever possible one's choice should be limited to one size for a particular purpose. The most convenient sizes are probably 75 × 25 mm (3″ × 1″) flat bottomed glass tubes for general collecting and transporting insects, and 40 × 10 mm (1½″ × ⅜″) or 50 × 12·5 mm (2″ × ½″) flat bottomed tubes with natural corks or plastic stoppers for collecting specimens into preserving fluids.

Some collectors, lepidopterists in particular, prefer to collect into glass bottomed or plastic 'pill' boxes which are specially made for entomological purposes. The glass bottomed boxes are usually supplied in 'nests', one size inside the next largest, in size ranges from 25 – 65 mm (1″–2½″) in diameter. This method of capture relies on the insects flying up from their position of rest when disturbed by the collector, into the box which has been placed over them or in their direct flight path. The lid is placed over the open end and the captured insect secured.

Haversacks, or special collecting coats

All the above equipment, plus nets, killing bottles etc, are most easily carried in a haversack when in the field. A stout canvas bag may usually be purchased at very little cost and adapted to the requirements of the collector. Straps should be sewn onto the inner walls to hold the more fragile equipment, killing bottles, alcohol containers etc. The bag should have shoulder straps of a suitable length to enable it to be carried on the collector's back, leaving both hands free, but securely anchored to ensure that it does not swing round to the front when the bearer bends down or leans forward.

An alternative means of carrying equipment is provided by a 'collecting coat', which may range from an old greatcoat or jacket with conveniently large pockets, to a modified or specially constructed waistcoat with a large number of additional pockets. The latter garment is more comfortable to wear in warmer conditions and is particularly useful when large numbers of individual killing bottles or tubes are used in collecting, as when collecting around a light at night.

Aspirators, 'pooters' or sucking-tubes

One of the simplest and most efficient pieces of apparatus for collecting small insects is the aspirator or 'pooter'. It may be used to remove insects from a sweep-net or to collect them directly from vegetation, mud, litter, on bark etc.

There are a multitude of designs, but only two fundamental types, those that rely on the direct sucking of air through the aspirator so that insects are drawn into a collecting chamber, and the type in which, by blowing air through the aspirator insects are drawn in on a current of air; the methods of operation are totally different, but the end result is the same.

The aspirators working on a direct sucking action, Fig. 4 are easily constructed, their working principal being the same. Insects are drawn into the chamber through the entry tube, and the exit tube from the chamber, through which air is withdrawn, is closed to the captured insects by a piece of muslin or gauze secured across the aperture. The type shown in Fig. 4 (C) may be adapted, using a shorter inlet tube and narrower cork, to fit the standard 25 mm (1″) diameter flat-bottomed tubes. A short glass or plastic mouth-piece is usually attached to the rubber tubing when the aspirator is operated by mouth. The alternative method of providing suction is by the use of a suction bulb, consisting of a rubber bulb with suitable valves. The use of the bulb is in most cases less efficient, as less sucking power is produced, but in certain circumstances and situations it is both safer and more pleasant to use, ie when insects are to be collected from an unpleasant pabulum, eg faecal matter, carrion, etc. In very dry and dusty areas the inclusion of a dust-trap between the mouthpiece and the pooter is advised. The trap consists of a simple glass or plastic bulb into which wadding is loosely packed to act as a dust filter.

There are circumstances when, due to the health hazard, the direct sucking type of aspirator should never be used. Such situations are rarely encountered, except by the specialist collector, but as a general rule direct-sucking aspirators should not be used in caves, bat roosts or in removing insects from bird or mammal nests.

The second type of aspirator is usually called a 'blow-pooter', Fig. 4 (B). This aspirator requires some skill in glass blowing to

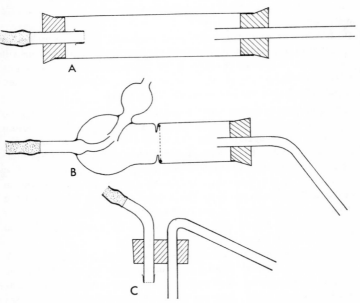

FIG. 4. Insect aspirators, or pooters. A, Sucking, tubular form; B, Blowing form; C, Sucker form for fitting into bottle.

17

produce and most collectors will probably prefer to order the apparatus from an entomological supplier. The apparatus functions as follows. Air is blown down the rubber tubing from the mouthpiece which leads into a narrowing curved tube. The air jet is directed into the mouth of the outlet tube which is of approximately twice the diameter. A vortex produced in the bulb of the outlet tube draws air rapidly from the main chamber of the aspirator and as a consequence any insect close to the inlet tube is drawn into the collecting chamber. The collecting chamber is sealed from the main chamber by a platform of fine gauze supported on a stout wire ring and secured to the supporting projections with a water soluble adhesive. The suction produced by this type of aspirator is not as powerful as that of the direct sucking aspirator. It is possible by placing the thumb or fore finger over the aperture of the outlet tube to use this apparatus also as a direct-sucking aspirator.

Both types of aspirator work most efficiently when air is drawn rapidly into the collecting chambers, as a long slow influx of air will cause most insects to cling firmly to the substratum. Exceptions must be made for very small or fragile insects which may be damaged if they are drawn into the aspirator too rapidly.

Killing insects in an aspirator is best carried out by introducing the vapour of one of the volatile fluids, see p. 47, into the collecting chamber; ethyl acetate, ether or carbon tetrachloride are most commonly used. There is no problem when using the 'blow-pooter' or the suction bulb attachment on a direct suction aspirator. The inlet tube of the apparatus is placed above the fluid, never in contact with the liquid, and the vapour is drawn in. When the insects in the chamber become comatose they may be safely removed to a killing jar where they should be left for a sufficient time to ensure their death.

Insects in the direct suction mouth-operated aspirator should not be killed in this way, as vapour may accidentally be drawn into the lungs. It must be remembered that all the fluids used to kill insects are harmful to man. Vapour of the killing agents may be drawn into the aspirator in a number of ways, the simplest is to replace the glass or plastic mouthpiece with a rubber bulb, place a small piece of cotton wool or filter paper soaked in an appropriate killing agent into the aperture of the inlet tube, and draw in the vapour by compressing and releasing the rubber bulb. Alternatively a partial vacuum can be induced in the aspirator as follows. The rubber tubing is gripped close to the connection with the exit tube of the aspirator with the thumb and fore finger of both hands. The left hand retains its grip while the thumb and fore finger of the right hand are moved along the tube towards the mouthpiece compressing the tube as they progress, and expelling the air in the tube, to produce a partial vacuum. The fore finger and thumb of the left hand are released and vapour is drawn into the chamber of the aspirator. This action should be repeated a number of times to fill the chamber. Tobacco smokers have an alternative method at their disposal, as smoke may be blown directly into the aspirator to stupefy the catch before it is removed to a killing bottle. Care should be taken with this method as the smoke usually has a high water content which may condense and spoil the catch.

The modern use of plastic aspirator barrels makes the choice of killing agents very important, since many plastics are dissolved or rendered opaque by the organic agents commonly used. Whichever method is used it is important to remember that the insects in the aspirator should be removed as soon as possible after they become comatose, and the apparatus cleaned thoroughly at regular intervals.

Care should be taken never to collect insects of greatly differing sizes and robustness, as the more fragile specimens invariably suffer damage in the close confinement of the aspirator. Never collect too many specimens at one time and if numbers of very active insects are taken a piece of crumpled paper placed in the collecting chamber will reduce the degree of contact between the individuals by increasing the area over which they may crawl. It should be remembered that many predatory insects are not deterred in their search for prey by being confined in an aspirator, and noted predators should be removed from the chamber as soon as possible after capture.

Nets

A wide variety of nets are available to the collector and the type used is very much a matter of preference. Only the basic types of net and their use are considered here.

General purpose nets Such nets may have a solid or folding frame and the choice of either is dependent upon the purpose to which it is to be put, ease of transport, and storage when not in use. The solid frames are usually made of cane, ash, nylon or metal, the latter being preferred by the majority of collectors. Folding frames are usually made of metal, often of spring-steel. Net handles, in length and composition, are again a matter of preference. However, most collectors find that very long handled nets, longer than one metre (*c*. 3 ft) are very unwieldy, although sometimes useful for collecting insects on the inflorescences of trees or in deep gullies. Net bags are generally made of closely woven material, the size of the mesh depending upon the collectors interests, the larger the size of the insects to be collected the larger the net mesh. Nets for general collecting must be able to retain even the smallest insects. Fine mesh nets are usually made of cotton, in the form of organdie, but this material is difficult to obtain and has been largely replaced by the man-made fibres, nylon and terylene so far as purchased ones are concerned. Unlike cotton products the latter are largely rot proof although they are affected by sunlight and some organic chemicals, and some collectors maintain that they are not as strong as the natural products. Organdie bags are not difficult to make for oneself. A white net bag is most commonly used for general collecting, dark green or black being preferred by those collecting predominantly pale insects, eg Lepidoptera, as the latter are more easily seen against a dark background.

The length of the bag should be at least twice the diameter, so that when the net frame is turned at the end of a stroke, the bottom section is sealed by its own weight (Fig. 5 (A)) and captured insects prevented from escaping.

Once the capture has been made and the insect trapped in the net, it must then be transferred to the killing-bottle. The insect may be induced to move into the bottom of the net by holding the bag end of the net towards the sun or by rapidly sweeping the bag through the air. The bag end can then be closed off from the remainder of the net by gathering the net material above it, in the hand. If a

20

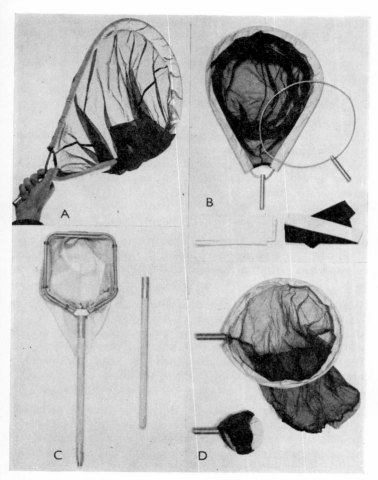

Fig. 5. Nets. A, Kite, folded; B, Kite and ring of circular net with spare sweeping bag (left) and aerial bag (right); Pond net and extension handle; D, spring steel folding net, folded and open.

killing-bottle is inserted into the bag and the mouth pushed into the pocket formed as above, the insect is given no opportunity to escape. Alternatively, the lower closed portion of the bag can be placed in a large killing-jar and the cork partially replaced. After a suitable period, depending upon the susceptibility of the insect to the killing-agent, and when the captive is comatose, the net may be taken from the jar and the insect removed to the killing-jar once again to complete the process.

If numbers of small insects are taken in the net they may be removed with an aspirator. The captures are forced into the bottom of the net by rapidly sweeping the net through the air, and the insects picked up with the aspirator as they fly or crawl up to the mouth of the net. If the net is of a sufficient diameter it is usually easier to place one's head and upper arms in the net mouth, thereby greatly reducing the area through which flying insects can escape.

Kite or balloon nets These are large nets of a distinctive shape (Fig. 5 (A, B)) used almost exclusively for collecting Lepidoptera and Odonata. Kite net bags are usually several times as long as wide.

Water-nets For collecting aquatic insects a stoutly built net is used (Fig. 5 (D)). A water-net is usually of smaller diameter and shallower than general purpose nets, and has a bag of much stouter material. The ideal material for water-net bags is bolting-silk, but this is prohibitively expensive, and nylon, hessian, or calico are usually used as alternatives. See also section on aquatic insects, p. 63.

Sweep nets These are specially strengthened nets for collecting insects that habitually hide in dense vegetation, and which usually fly only when disturbed. The resistance to the passage of the net, and the abrasive nature of the vegetation requires that both the net frame and the net bag be strengthened. It is usual to use a rigid frame for a sweep-net and for really heavy sweeping the frame may be further supported by securing the handle across the frame rather than attaching it to a single point. The rim of the bag is protected by a strip of leather or thin metal, or by using a more hard wearing material for the upper two or three inches of the bag.

Alternatively, the bag may be hung from the frame by metal rings so that the metal frame alone takes the force of the sweeping.

Specimens secured with the sweep-net are dealt with as described for the general purpose net, see p. 20.

Sweep netting

This is the most commonly used technique for mass collecting, the only equipment required being a stoutly made net, an aspirator and a killing-bottle.

The technique is simple; the sweep-net is worked back and forth through the vegetation, the mouth of the net being kept in contact with the vegetation by twisting the net around at the end of each stroke. Sweeping should always be carried out into the wind to minimise the chances of the net being turned inside out. At the end of a series of sweeps, insects in the net may be forced into the lower half of the bag by sweeping the net vigorously through the air, and specimens collected into pill boxes or 75×25 mm ($3'' \times 1''$) tubes, or with an aspirator by placing the mouth of the net over the head and aspirating specimens as they crawl or fly towards the opening (see page 16.) An alternative method for taking small or very active insects is to force the catch into the bottom of the net bag, as described above, the complete lower end is then placed into a wide mouthed killing-jar until the net occupants are stupefied. With practice it is possible to leave the insects in the killing-bottle for just sufficient time so as to stun them, the catch may then be sorted and after retaining those specimens required, the remainder may be released so that they may recover later.

Sweep netting should never be used when vegetation is wet, as insects become wetted and adhere to the net and to one another. In very dry climates, especially in the dry summer months sweeping is often difficult due to aestivating snails. Many terrestrial snails aestivate above ground on vegetation and are collected in large numbers in the net, severely damaging the insects taken with them. In such situations, the contents should be inspected after every two or three strokes of the net. Similar difficulties are encountered when sweeping grasses in flower and plants bearing fruiting struc-

23

tures.   In such cases pollen and loose seeds may coat or damage the catch and it is again necessary to sweep for only short periods before removing the captured insects.

Beating

While sweep netting is particularly useful for capturing small or cryptic insects that fly when disturbed, beating is designed to capture those insects, notably beetles, plant bugs and larvae, that do not, or cannot, fly.   Many of the latter group are rarely collected by sweeping as they fall from the vegetation when disturbed and feign death. Equipment required consists of a beating tray and stout stick and collecting apparatus, either tubes, pill boxes or aspirator.

Beating trays. A number of designs are available, ranging from simple sheets of cotton, nylon or plastic which are simply laid under the vegetation, to rigid trays with handles.   A convenient portable tray is shown in Fig. 6 in which triangular pockets are sewn on the four corners of a square sheet of any of the materials mentioned. All four pockets open towards the centre of the square.   Two sticks are inserted diagonally into the pockets providing both a handle and a rigid frame.   Two bamboos of convenient length may be carried as part of the kit, or saplings cut from surrounding vegetation; the square sheet is easily folded for transporting.   An old umbrella will serve a useful dual purpose, either as a beating tray or as protection against inclement weather.

When beating, care must be taken in holding or arranging the tray so that the vegetation is disturbed as little as possible before the tray is in position.   Even a shadow falling across some beetles may cause them to drop from the vegetation.

The colour of the beating tray is a matter of personal preference. Some collectors maintain that certain species become agitated when they land on light coloured surfaces although the reverse is definitely the case with many small plant-feeding groups.   The odd handful of grass or leaves placed in the centre of the tray before beating commences, provides a refuge for specimens that might otherwise attempt to escape.

Specimens from the tray may be taken directly into the killing-bottle, collected into pillboxes, tubes or removed by aspirator.

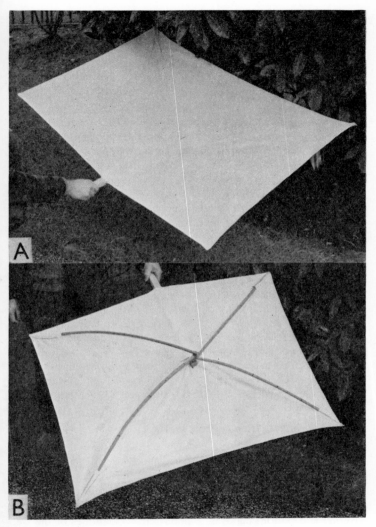

FIG. 6.   Beating tray;   A, upper side;   B, underside

Small soft-bodied species, eg Thysanoptera and Psocoptera, should be collected directly into alcohol, picked up by means of a camel hair brush, mounted-needle or suitable alternative, eg a blade of grass.

Sieving

Sieving leaf litter, friable earth, bases of grass tussocks, driftline and flood refuse etc, is a very good method of acquiring the larger cryptic species as an adjunct to separation by Berlese funnel. Sets of graded sieves are available from a number of suppliers of chemical apparatus although only the coarser grades are suitable for sorting organic litter.

Litter from a particular habitat should be passed through a large garden riddle with an aperture of 1 cm to remove the larger debris. The sievings may then be searched by placing one handful at a time of coarse sieved debris on a translucent or white polythene sheet and the larger insects removed using a tube or aspirator. The debris may then either be subjected to further graded sievings each fraction being searched separately, or be placed in a Berlese funnel to extract the remaining insects (see page 27). As the major part of the process of separation of insects from litter is more conveniently carried out in the laboratory or at home, the litter samples should be collected in linen bags. Linen is preferable to polythene bags, although these may be used, as the latter tends to compact the litter or soil samples if they have any appreciable moisture content. (Care should be taken in storing the bags for transport as close packing also causes compacting). The bags should be securely tied to prevent mixing during transporting and labelled both on the inside and outside.

Extracting insects from organic matter

Wet extraction. Two basic methods are used in the wet extraction of insects from soils and plant detritus, namely sieving and flotation. Both techniques are only really useful for collecting larvae, Coleoptera and other insects that are to be stored in fluid.

Wet sieving is a useful method of removing small insects from soils, riverine and bottom deposits in ponds etc. Quantities of the wet materials are flushed through a nest of sieves with water and the various graded samples sorted under a little water in a shallow tray. If large quantities of plant debris are present the sieved samples may have to be subjected to extraction by flotation.

A number of complex techniques have been developed for extraction by flotation where the methods used are a means of quantitative sampling but very few are applicable to field collecting. Basically, an attempt is made to separate the plant and animal materials by differential flotation in a solution of an inorganic salt in water, eg magnesium sulphate, or differential wetting and floating in a mixture of two immiscible liquids, usually water and an organic solvent. It is impossible to be dogmatic as to the best method to use, the appropriate chemical depending largely on the state of the materials to be separated. The amount of water already absorbed by the material and the volume of the entrapped air all have a bearing on the density of the material and the method used.

The most straightforward method is simply to stir the sample of dung or plant debris in a 25 per cent solution of magnesium sulphate and to skim the insects from the surface. The advantage of using strong solutions of inorganic salts in differential flotation is that when extracted and removed quickly, and washed in fresh water, many insect larvae are unharmed and may be bred through to the adult stage.

Extraction by differential wetting is carried out by shaking the material to be separated with a mixture of petrol or paraffin (kerosene). The plant debris remains in the water layer while the insects, whose cuticles are 'wetted' by the organic fluid float in the petrol or paraffin layer above the water. The insects in fluid are decanted from the vessel, washed in a suitable solvent eg ether, and dried.

Dry extraction This is used on soils and plant debris of all types. The extracting agent may be a rising temperature and a steady reduction in humidity, or chemical agents which act as irritants and increase the mobility of the insects, driving them from the samples.

The classic apparatus for extracting insects from litter and soil, and generally the only feasible field apparatus is the Berlese funnel with the Tullgren modification. The apparatus consists of a funnel with a coarse mesh gauze platform across the top on which the samples to be extracted are placed (Fig. 7). The funnel should be

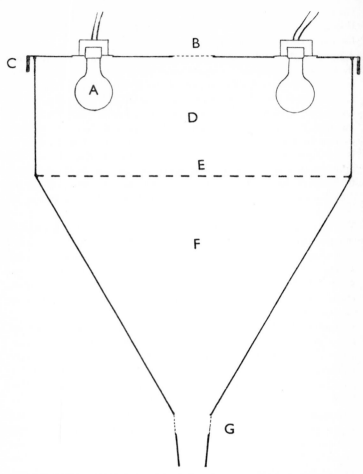

FIG. 7. Tulgren funnel. A, Light bulb heating source; B, Ventilator gauze; C, Heavy overlapping lid; D, Upper chamber; E, Metal gauze for receiving sample; F, Lower chamber; G, Lower ventilator gauze.

28

as large as is convenient, for the larger the funnel the larger the sample that can be extracted. Large samples dry out gradually and allow the smaller and more delicate insects time to make their way through the sample. The heat source is usually one or a number of light bulbs, depending on the size of the apparatus, mounted in a cover that fits over the funnels. An aperture in the cover, covered with fine mesh to exclude flying insects attracted to the light, is advisable to ensure some ventilation and reduce 'sweating' in the samples. The base of the funnel leads into a collecting jar containing the preserving fluid, usually 70 per cent alcohol.

The materials to be extracted are placed on the gauze tray, the lid placed over them and the lights switched on *before* the collecting jars are put in place. Reversal of the procedure results in a quantity of fine particles falling into the preserving fluid. Where possible the samples should be graded and rough sorted before extraction to remove the larger Arthropods and minimise the disturbance of the litter on the tray.

An alternative method of heating the samples is by using a jacketed funnel, usually made of copper, through which hot water is circulated. The water may be heated in an adjacent reservoir tank by an immersion coil or in the absence of a source of electrical power by a small flame as supplied by a spirit lamp. J T Salmon (1946) has described the construction and use of an excellent portable funnel of this type for field use.

Whatever method of heating is used the samples should not be allowed to overheat or become too dry as many species of the more delicate insects will die *in situ* and be lost to the collector.

Chemical extraction The use of certain chemical irritants, eg 'tear gas' is suggested by some field-workers for driving insects through the funnels in damp and difficult conditions in the tropics. This cannot be recommended as general practice because of the unpleasant and dangerous nature of the substances used.

Thrips and other small cryptic insects may be extracted from flower heads, inflorescences, porous fungi etc by the use of turpentine vapour. A plug of cotton wool soaked in spirit of turpentine is wedged into a second funnel of similar size to the Berlese funnel.

29

The plant material is placed on the gauze tray of the Berlese funnel and the second funnel inverted over it. Turpentine vapour rapidly permeates the inflorescences, fungi, etc, and the insects are driven out, passing through the gauze into the collecting jar. This method is extremely rapid and extraction is usually complete within an hour. It is doubted whether this technique is applicable to dense soil and litter samples and to the extraction of delicate and soft bodied insects.

TRAPPING

Increasingly in recent years, use has been made of trapping methods both for collecting insects and for studying their behaviour, populations, etc. It is convenient when considering the various traps to consider them as two distinct types.

The first type, the 'active' traps, are those in which attractants are used, eg light, colours, chemical and natural baits. The 'passive' type of trap makes use of certain natural characteristics of the insects and, in fact, they are instrumental in their own capture, eg pitfall traps, window, Malaise and Herting traps.

Active Trapping

Light traps There are a wide variety of light trap designs described in entomological literature, all based on the principal that nocturnal insects are attracted to light, especially light at the blue end of the spectrum. References are given below to a number of light traps, some of them used extremely successfully by their originators. Only one design is considered here in any detail, the Robinson trap now in general use among entomologists, together with a variant, the small portable Heath trap.

Robinson trap This apparatus (see Fig. 8) may be used, where electric current is available, with the mercury vapour lamp for which it was designed. Where a steady current is not available paraffin (kerosene) or petrol (gasolene) pressure lamps or a battery supplied lamp may be used as alternatives. The light source lies in the centre of four radial vanes fixed to the inner side of an inverted funnel resting on the rim of a cone forming the lid of a wide shallow cylinder. On the bottom of this cylinder below the opening in the funnel, is a shallow funnel surrounding a perforated area through which rain water may drain away. Insects attracted to the light, fly or fall through the lower opening into the cylinder below. Crumpled paper, or more successfully cardboard egg boxes, placed in the cylinder provide the trapped insects with a promenade and hiding places into which they may crawl. The captured insects are anaesthetised in the trap by using tetrachlorethane vapour emanating from a small container on the floor of the cylinder. A small spirit lamp with a short wick is particularly suitable for this purpose.

When using a mercury-vapour lamp it is important that a 'choke' should be included in the circuit.

Light traps will catch completely different types of insect fauna depending on the climatic conditions. On warm humid nights, or in the tropics, Lepidoptera represent a far lower percentage of

Fig. 8. Robinson light trap. (Photo Watkins & Doncaster).

the total catch. On cooler evenings, or generally in the cool temperature regions, Lepidoptera make up a higher percentage of the catch. Insects are rarely attracted to light on bright moonlit nights, and other local factors, wind direction and intensity may also affect the catch. The optimum conditions and position for light trapping in any particular habitat may best be found by trial and error.

Due to the difficulties encountered in making the Robinson trap in metal the trap has recently been modified and produced in nylon and plastic.

Heath Trap This is a small portable version of the Robinson trap with a weight of less than 3 kg (6 lb). It uses a 6 watt, 230 mm (9″) fluorescent tube emitting a continuous band of ultra-violet light, just extending into the visible spectrum, and works off two 6 volt motor-cycle 'wet' batteries, which may be carried in a shoulder rucksack. 12 Ah batteries give up to twelve hours running without re-charging. The trap consists of a 250 mm (10″) cubical aluminium chamber with a drainage aperture in the base and a larger circular aperture in the top into which a truncated polythene cone is fitted. The fluorescent tube, mounted in tri-radiate baffles, stands in the cone. Apart from its lightness, the advantage of this type of trap is its relatively low running temperature, ie the light source is not damaged by sudden cooling due to rain. The whole trap can be dismantled and folded flat into a space of 300 × 250 × 150 mm (12″ × 10″ × 6″).

One of the disadvantages of using a light trap is the relatively poor condition of many of the captured insects. Unless a powerful anaesthetising agent is used, predacious insects, ants, beetles, etc may enter the trap and damage the catch, or larger moths damage smaller ones by continual agitated motion. Non-lepidopterous insects are invariably covered in loose scales, although many of these may be removed by washing in absolute alcohol and ether.

Moth sheet Although this is not a true trapping technique it is convenient to mention this method here.

A moth sheet consists of a large white sheet which is placed horizontally on the ground or vertically between supports. If the latter method is used a portion of the sheet is allowed to extend onto the ground, providing a means of access to the light for those insects that do not readily fly and an area of reduced light intensity for those insects that rarely settle close to the light source. A light source, such as a paraffin or petrol vapour lamp, or if a reliable source of light is available, m.v., or black light fluorescent tubes, is placed in the centre of the sheet or suspended in front of the sheet, depending on the method adopted.

Insects attracted to the light are taken, either by tube or aspirator, or with a net if they refuse to settle. As suggested above, many species are attracted to the lighted area, but do not attend the light, or make only a fleeting visit and alight in the twilight area. To capture such species the environs of the sheet should be inspected at regular intervals.

Use of the moth sheet is particularly valuable when collecting small or fragile specimens which invariably become damaged in the conventional light trap.

Warning. Ultra-violet light is damaging to the eyes and precautions must be taken not to look directly at the light source if it is inadequately screened, for this reason damaged tubes or bulbs may be dangerous.

Baited traps The use of baited traps is a very efficient method of collecting specific groups of insects, and by the judicious use of baits it is possible to extract certain types of insect from the general fauna. The traps themselves may be as simple or as complex as the collector wishes. Simple pitfall type traps are easily constructed for terrestrial groups and although invariably equally efficaceous in attracting flying insects, the majority of such traps are not designed to facilitate their collection. Traps designed to collect groups of flying insects are slightly more complex, the majority relying on attracting insects into the trap and then upon their inability to retrace their route and escape.

Baited pitfall traps This type is the simplest of traps, consisting of a straight sided container that is sunk level with the surface of the surrounding substratum. A number of insects will, of course, fall into the trap even if it is left unbaited (see page 36) but when baited, the trap will attract insects from a wider area. Pitfall traps must be protected from rainfall and from larger animals. This is most easily done by covering the trap with a heavy stone supported on a number of smaller stones to allow access to the insects (see Fig. 9) or by covering with a suitable alternative, eg thorny brushwood.

Almost all natural baits are suitable for pitfall traps, fruit, dung, offal or carrion being particularly successful. A weak formalin solution, approximately 3 per cent, has the dual advantage of acting as an attractant, and in killing and preserving the insects that it attracts. Insects killed in formalin should be transferred to alcohol as soon as possible, washed and dried. Prolonged storage in formalin results in the breakdown of insect cuticle unless the formalin is buffered (see page 58). If difficulties are experienced with predation by the larger ground running insects of smaller insects in the trap, a screen of perforated zinc should be placed on supports in the bottom of the trap, below which the smaller species may take refuge.

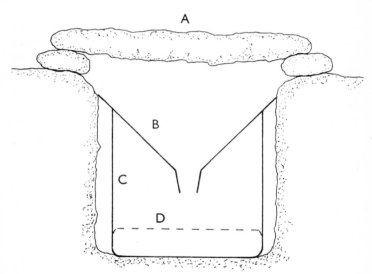

FIG. 9. Baited pitfall trap. A, Covering stone; B, Funnel; C, Trap container; D, Gauze screen to segregate catch.

Baited traps for flying insects A whole variety of trap designs are available, but the type used must depend upon the materials available, the habitat that is being searched, and the group of insects required. A simple pattern is shown in Fig. 10 and consists of a bait reservoir below, perforated to allow insects to enter, and an upper chamber in which they congregate when attempting to escape. The majority of such traps, with their sophisticated modifications, are suspended from trees or other supports to minimise interference from ground living insects and other animals. As the only point of access is along the suspending wire or cord, intrusion from this quarter, by ants, etc, may be minimised by adding a grease trap or greasing the wire or cord.

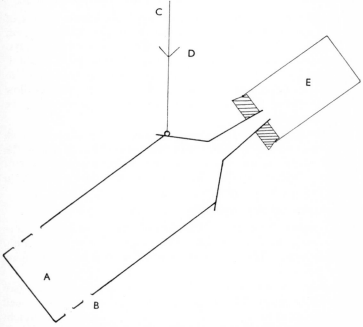

FIG. 10. Baited trap for flying insects. A, Bait chamber; B, Entry apertures; C, Suspending wire; D, Grease trap; E, Capturing chamber.

Most of the natural baits, eg fruit, fungi, dung, rotting eggs, sugars and a variety of artificial chemical attractants are suitable for use with the suspended traps. Amyl acetate, in the form of liquid-soaked wadding or as sweets (pear-drops), is particularly attractive to Lepidoptera, Diptera and Hymenoptera. The majority of fruits and fungi, especially when fermenting are powerful attractants to a number of groups.

Traps, wherever possible, should be sited in shade to reduce both condensation effects and the damaging action of direct sunlight on the traps and the catch. Natural baits are, of course, most efficient in areas where there is little of the bait available to the insect fauna. In dry climates it is important to ensure that the baits are prevented from drying out as this substantially reduces their attractiveness.

Coloured trays A novel method of attracting certain groups of insects, namely Homoptera, (particularly aphids), small Diptera, Hymenoptera and Coleoptera is by the use of coloured trays. Shallow trays of various colours, bright yellow being most successful, are filled with water to which a little detergent has been added to reduce the surface tension. Insects attracted to the bright yellow surface become trapped in the water from which they may be removed at leisure.

This technique was first developed for sampling Aphid populations. The attractiveness of the yellow surface is thought to be due to the insects mistaking the yellow colour for certain pigments in plant tissues. Different shades and intensities of yellow will attract a variety of species and groups.

Non-baited 'passive' trapping

Grouped here are trapping techniques relying almost entirely either upon insects inadvertently entering into the traps, or upon certain of their innate behavioural characteristics that lead to their ultimate capture.

Fall-traps Baited fall-traps have already been mentioned (see page 33). Unbaited fall-traps are very successful if positioned carefully in suitable habitats. A simple trap consists of a straight sided container buried to rim level and covered with a large stone with smaller stones as supports. The covering stone acts as protection against rain or wind-blown sand and is itself attractive as cover to many ground-living insects.

Positioning of the traps is particularly important in country with difficult terrain, eg loose sand or rock, and dense vegetation, where most ground-inhabiting insects frequent paths, gulleys and dried river beds. Traps sited along these passage-ways produce far greater catches than those randomly scattered. In dry areas of soft soil and sand or wind-swept regions, artificial gulleys, wind breaks etc, may be constructed, each system leading to traps. In this way insects may be collected from a very large catchment area (see page 146).

The production of artificial habitats to facilitate collecting is a technique particularly useful in difficult conditions. Shade is of paramount importance in desert regions, most insects becoming nocturnal to reduce the dangers of desiccation. Bundles of closely packed vegetation, left in suitable gulleys, river beds etc, will act as focis and congregation points for nocturnal ground-running insects, and should be inspected during the first hours of daylight.

Herting trap This is a relatively simple trap consisting of a broad rectangular tent, 2 m high × 2 m broad × 1·3 m deep, with a flat roof. The two narrow sides and the roof are made from black sheet polythene, the front from translucent polythene and the back is left open. The whole structure is rigidly supported by four corner tent poles with guy ropes and a connecting cross pole to support the translucent side. Dr Herting of the Commonwealth Institute for Biological Control, Delemont, Switzerland, has perfected the use of this trap and gives the following suggestions for its use.

'The trap is set out with the front facing the light and as far as possible against the wind. There should be some cover and shade close behind it eg, the periphery of a wood, bushes, or even a single tree. Insects can enter the trap freely from behind and they fly towards the lighted front. They do not tend to move away from the front for if they do, they are confronted by the black polythene of the sides and roof and the diminished light intensity of the wooded area behind.'

This type of trap is particularly successful for catching large, fast flying Diptera and Hymenoptera, but not those insects that habitually patrol an area and are capable of completely reversing their flight direction when confronted with an obstacle. Trapped insects have to be collected individually from the translucent face.

As Herting (1969) mentions in his paper on the above trap, the 'Herting' trap is in fact, a variation upon the 'cheesecloth flight trap' of H B Leech (1955).

Malaise traps The Malaise trap is now an accepted and important part of the field collector's equipment. Since the original description by Dr Réné Malaise in 1937, a number of important modifications have been developed and published. It is quite out of the question in this publication to discuss these modifications and interested collectors should consult the references. These publications range from the detailed and fully comprehensive construction details of Townes (1962), to the development of an eminently portable and inexpensive version, Butler (1965), constructed from a 'mosquito-bed-net'.

The Malaise trap takes advantage of the simple fact that when the majority of flying insects meet an obstacle they attempt to fly up and around it rather than reverse their direction of flight. On entering a trap an insect flies into the centre partition and then proceeds to fly or crawl upwards, eventually becoming trapped at the highest point. The killing unit placed at this point receives the captive insects. Generally Diptera, Hymenoptera and Lepidoptera, in that order, predominate in Malaise trap catches. Coleoptera and many Hemiptera fall to the ground on hitting the centre partition, and unless a sealed floor area is included in the trap, beetles and bugs invariably escape under the edges of the trap.

The basic Malaise trap pattern is capable of being endlessly modified and improved according to the needs and whims of the collector. The simple model described below is based on a design that may be attributed in part to H Townes of the University of Michigan, who has done much to improve on the original Malaise plan, including a vastly superior killing-jar assembly. In addition to this latter structure, a further device, intended to guide the captured insects to a killing-jar buried in the ground below the trap, Fig. 11 must be

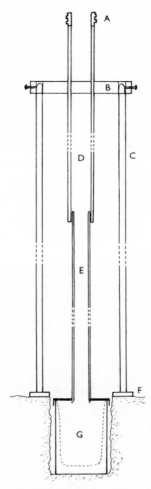

FIG. 11. McAlpine's extension for Malaise trap. A, Point of attachment to reception chamber of Malaise trap; B, Holding ring for plastic tube and supporter rods; C, Telescoping support rods; D, Tube I; E, Tube II, fitting within tube I; F, Metal ring to support rods; G, Modified killing jar.

39

attributed to Dr J F McAlpine of the Canadian Department of Agriculture, Ottawa, (see page 39) who has kindly allowed this modification to be described here. Many modern traps are quadri-directional with a simple terminal collecting chamber.

The trap unit The trap may be constructed from any suitable fine-mesh netting, mosquito netting (bobbinet) being very good. Nylon and many other synthetic fibres are perfectly adequate, but deteriorate rapidly in bright sunlight. The colour of the netting is a matter of choice and there is conflicting evidence concerning the effect of coloured netting on the volume and composition of the catch. Malaise made his original traps from black cotton netting, but green or white traps are apparently equally successful.

The basic design is that of a tent (Figs 12, 13), the original inspiration for Malaise, with both long sides open and with the top sloping up on one side to the killing chamber. The size must depend upon available materials and the requirements of the collector, but, all

Fig. 12. Malaise trap.

things being equal, the longer the trap the greater the catch. However, if the trap is very tall some difficulty will be experienced in inspecting and replacing the collecting chamber, and the trap is more prone to wind interference and damage.

All the edges of the netting must be protected and strengthened with binding tape before they are sewn together. A frame of wood or aluminium poles is necessary to support the trap in the absence of suitable surrounding trees and branches, and to help in protecting the netting from wind damage. A supported trap has the added advantage that it can be erected in any difficult situation, hoisted to the canopy level in forested areas or lowered into gulleys or down cliff faces, and in other places where a collector is unable to follow.

Killing unit The killing unit (Fig. 14) is conveniently manufactured from two large screw-top polythene jars, the permanently fixed jar bearing a staked support and attached to the trap in the manner shown. The fixing collar between the jars is made from two screw-top lids with their centres removed and the rims firmly joined with a metal collar or a suitable adhesive. The lower replaceable jar contains the preserving fluid or killing agent. In

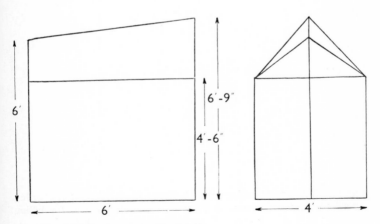

FIG. 13. Malaise trap assembly details.

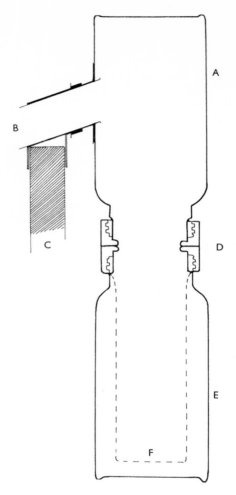

FIG. 14.   Malaise trap killing unit.   A, Reception chamber; B, connecting tunnel to trap; C, Supporting pole; D, Connecting device for killing chamber; E, Killing chamber; F, Inner metal gauze chamber.

warm and humid areas when the trap cannot be inspected at least once every two days, it may be necessary to collect directly into alcohol although this should be avoided whenever possible. The most convenient killing agent is dichlorvos, and a small piece of absorbent material impregnated with this material is placed in the jar. This material may be impaled on a piece of wire or a pin pushed through the wall or the jar, so that it is out of reach of the insects.

Dichlorvos has many advantages as a killing agent, it has reasonably quick 'knock down' and tends, initially, to induce paralysis in the captured insects rather than to kill them instantly, consequently reducing the length of time between their death and their removal for pinning or layering by the collector. The vapour from the dichlorvos is long lasting and does not coat or damage the insects in any way as do many other insecticides. Its major fault lies in its possible toxicity to the collector and it should only be used out-of-doors or in a well-ventilated room. It should not be allowed to come into contact with the skin.

Alternative killing agents may be used but all suffer from marked disadvantages. The organic vapours eg ethyl and methyl acetate, chloroform and carbon tetrachloride, evaporate rapidly from the killing-jar and become ineffective, and may affect plastics used in the trap construction. Cyanide has the disadvantage of having a poor 'knock down' in the low concentrations that develop in the open killing chambers, although it is long lasting. All the alternative agents may be used but generally require greater vigilance in their use, or modifications to the simple plan of the killing chamber.

Siting Much of the success of Malaise trapping is dependent upon the correct siting of the trap. Generally, insects tend to fly and congregate in specific situations, for example, along the edges of dense forest growth, along stream-banks, rides in woods and in gulleys. All but the more strongly flying insects are endangered by strong winds, most by even the lightest of winds. They react accordingly and avoid exposed and open situations, preferring sheltered gulleys and the leeward sides of wooded areas, hills etc.

A knowledge of the local topography and wind conditions is a useful aid when siting a trap. Traps placed in shaded areas should, if possible, have the killing chamber facing towards the light, to facilitate the rapid entry of trapped insects into the chamber.

As mentioned previously Coleoptera are often poorly represented in Malaise trap catches unless a covered floor area is included in the design. For those beetles and bugs unwilling or unable to climb the side netting, stones and logs may be laid on the floor to provide shelter, as well as additional weight to the structure. Flowers and vegetation placed in the entrances may help to induce flower frequenting species to enter the confines of the trap.

A large Malaise trap may successfully be used in conjunction with a light for night collecting. Of course the trap collects both day and night without additional attractants, but many insects that will normally briefly inspect a light source before flying off or settling some distance away, are caught in the trap. It is usually advisable to empty the killing chamber both at dusk and in the morning to segregate the day flying insects from the large numbers of moths that enter the trap at night.

Vacuum apparatus

Although it is not within the scope of this hand-book it is important to draw the collector's attention to recent advances in technique. Portable suction traps are now available for really large scale collecting and sampling of insect faunas. One apparatus works on the principle of a large vacuum cleaner and is powered by a portable two-stroke petrol engine carried on the collector's back. Insects are drawn into a wide extensible tube and filtered from the air stream by a series of graded nylon filters. As a method of collecting specimens for museum and study collections, or material for which identifications are required, the condition of the material obtained by this method leaves much to be desired, although if it is used carefully on dry vegetation and operated only for short periods, useful material of the more robust species of insects may be taken.

This apparatus is heavy, and this fact should be borne in mind when contemplating its use under tropical conditions or at high altitudes.

44

KILLING

Killing agents

There are a number of killing-agents that are available to the collector, but without exception they have certain disadvantages, apart from their obvious toxicity. Their use is in most part dependent upon the techniques preferred, and the groups to be collected. The most commonly used agents are listed below, together with a brief account of their chemical and physical properties, and precautions and methods for their use.

'**Cyanide**', as potassium or sodium cyanide, is a good all purpose killing-agent which by its slow hydrolisation produces hydrocyanic acid gas, causing most insects to die rapidly. The safest way for the collector to use cyanide is in a 'cyanide-jar', in which solid pieces of the chemical, preferably in an impure form, are sealed into the bottom of a wide mouthed jar with a plaster-of-paris and water mix. Freshly made jars have a tendency to 'sweat' and should be left unstoppered for 24 hours, and thereafter wiped out regularly with absorbent tissue, the latter being burnt after use. Cyanide killing-jars should be bought ready-made from entomological dealers, unless laboratory facilities are available to the collector to make his own.

Cyanide is extremely toxic and great care must be taken in its use, and in the disposal of the cyanide jar when it becomes exhausted. A cyanide-jar lasts for some time, the period depending on the frequency of use and the climatic conditions under which it is used. When expended it can frequently be given to the local public authorities who often have means for disposal of dangerous chemicals. Alternatively it may be placed in a bucket of water to which is added a solution of sodium hypochlorite or bleaching powder which converts the cyanide into non-poisonous substances after a few days. The contents should then be broken up and given the same treatment again.

Insects killed in a cyanide-jar are stiff and unsuitable for setting for some hours. The gas also affects some pigments, many yellows turning to orange and red if left in the jar for any length of time. A very few insects, some moths of the family Zygaenidae in particular, are quite resistant to the effects of cyanide and alternative killing agents must be used.

Laurel leaves Leaves and shoots of the true laurel or cherry laurel *Prunus laurocerasus* L. provide a convenient and relatively safe source of cyanide fumes. The young leaves are thoroughly bruised by beating them on a flat wooden board with a mallet, and cut up into strips before being placed in a killing-jar. Alternatively, the crushed leaves may be tied in a piece of muslin and suspended in the jar or pinned to the cork stopper. When loose leaves are used they should be anchored by circles of blotting paper which also help to absorb excess moisture. The laurel-jar is left for a few days to allow the chemical reactions to take place that make these jars so potent. The action of bruising the leaves results in the mixing of a glucoside and an hydrolysing agent present in the cell sap, the final result of which is to produce benzaldehyde and hydrocyanic acid. The benzaldehyde helps to keep specimens relaxed once they have been killed by the cyanide fumes. The greatest danger with using a laurel-jar is that delicate specimens may become over-relaxed and disintegrate, or that specimens become wetted in the rather damp conditions that can develop in this type of killing-jar. A laurel-jar has a number of advantages over the cyanide-jar, not least of these is the ease with which the contents of the spent jars may be destroyed. If used with care the relaxed and preserved condition of specimens killed by this means enables the collector to set and mount specimens at his convenience.

Chloroform produces a heavy vapour, that will burn if ignited. Killing-bottles and jars utilising chloroform may be made by impregnating rubber, in the form of rubber-bands, sponge or chips, with as much chloroform as it will absorb. Fumes will be given off slowly for some time, and the rubber may be re-impregnated a number of times before it starts to crumble and break down. Insects must be protected from contact with the rubber by means of a layer of cotton-wool held in place by circles of filter paper or other absorbent paper. Insects killed in chloroform harden and are difficult to pin and set, and must be removed to a relaxing-box as soon as possible.

Carbon tetrachloride produces a heavy non-inflammable vapour. Killing-bottles may be manufactured and used as for chloroform.

Ethylene tetrachloride produces a heavy non-inflammable vapour. Use as for chloroform.

Ethyl acetate or acetic ether produces a heavy highly inflammable vapour, with a flash point of $-5°C$. A killing-bottle may be made for use with ethyl acetate (or amyl acetate) as described for the use of chloroform, but substituting celluloid chips for the rubber. Insects killed in ethyl acetate die and stay in a very relaxed state and in most cases may be left for some time in the killing-jar before setting. Some pigments, however, are affected if left exposed to it for too long.

Ether produces a heavier than air, highly inflammable, vapour which is dangerously explosive when mixed with air. Ether is too volatile to make a really suitable substitute for ethyl acetate although many entomologists prefer it to the latter.

Ammonia The gas ammonia is slightly heavier than air and is non-inflammable. Ammonia is released from a strong solution of ammonium hydroxide and is a useful killing-agent in certain circumstances. Insects killed with fumes of ammonia or by injection of strong ammonium hydroxide, relative density 0·880, die in a relaxed state and remain so for some hours. Unfortunately, ammonia affects the colours of many insects and this rather limits its use. Very large insects, particularly large moths and beetles may be killed by direct injection of 0·880 ammonium hydroxide.

Hot Water As a means of killing insects near-boiling water is particularly suitable for large hard-bodied species and for some groups of larvae that are ultimately to be stored in liquid preservatives. It should never be used for any insect bearing hairs or scales, nor where colouring is due to fine dusting, ie never for adult Trichoptera, Lepidoptera or Diptera.

There are a number of other organic fluids that may be used as killing-agents and insects may be subjected to vapour arising from the liquid or in a few cases totally immersed in the fluid. Where vapour is used, suitable all purpose killing-bottles may be prepared

47

as follows: plaster-of-paris mix is poured into a suitable container. The size of the container is usually dependent upon the insect groups for which the killing-bottle is required. A large-mouthed jar is used for most groups, but smaller jars and even tubes may be more suitable for smaller insects that are taken individually. A layer of plaster of 20–30 mm is usually sufficient for most purposes and the killing fluid is added to the plaster after it has thoroughly dried, until it will absorb no more. The life of the jar from a single charging depends upon the volatility of the fluid, and for most organic fluids is short. Insects should be protected from contact with the plaster by means of layers of cellulose wadding – never cotton wool – or with circles of filter paper or other absorbent paper. This type of killing-bottle works equally well with all the organic killing-fluids mentioned.

Precautions to be taken

In addition to the safety rules to be observed concerning the uses of toxic chemicals, there are a number of precautions that should be observed when using killing-bottles or jars.

The bottle must not be allowed to become wet inside, either from condensation or from the injudicious use of killing fluids. Never allow the bottle to stand in direct sunlight. The inside should be wiped out regularly with rag or blotting paper, and care taken in the disposal of the cleaning materials. Crumpled tissue paper should be placed in the killing-bottle when collecting small or fragile insects, to prevent them becoming damaged by abrasive contact with one another.

A killing-bottle having once been used to kill Lepidoptera should never be used for any other insects, as the latter may be spoiled by becoming coated with loose scales.

As many larger insects, especially Orthoptera and Coleoptera, regurgitate food and defaecate whilst dying, they are best killed in a separate container. It is a good policy to use a number of killing-bottles when collecting and whenever possible to segregate the catch before killing. Hymenoptera, eg wasps and ants, and many large and predaceous Coleoptera may severely damage other insects during their death throes.

Always remove insects from the killing-bottle at the earliest opportunity, as many of the killing-agents available cause irreversible colour changes and other unfortunate side effects.

MOUNTING, PRESERVING AND PACKING

After their capture it is very important that specimens are dealt with as rapidly and as carefully as possible to ensure their worth as objects of lasting scientific interest. Nothing is more depressing to the museum worker than to receive extensive collections from areas of outstanding interest only to find that the material has been damaged while being transported, on account of bad mounting or inadequate preserving and packing.

Pinning

Very few groups of insects demand more than the most simple packing and preserving techniques. Two groups of adult insects, however, require a little more effort and should be pinned in the field, these are Diptera (flies) and Lepidoptera (moths). The larger flies and moths should be pinned with a suitable grade of continental pin directly through the thorax. With Diptera the pin should be passed to one side of the mid line to ensure that at least one half of the rows of bristles and hairs remain intact. Smaller flies and moths (the 'microlepidoptera'), are pinned in a similar manner to the larger specimens, but with short, headless stainless steel points called 'minuten' (see p. 104, and p. 126). Very small Diptera may be placed between layers of cellulose wadding as described below. The smallest if pinned are best impaled on the points only of the minuten, and in the field rather than later (see p. 126).

All other groups of insects, with the exception of those delicate insects which are papered, in which the adults are preserved dry are ultimately either pinned, or mounted on card points. These operations may be performed at a later date and there is no need for pinning in the field.

There was at one time in the recent past a large variety of pins available to the entomologist, but it is now becoming increasingly difficult to buy suitable pins. Wherever possible, ie where a pin penetrates insect tissues, stainless steel pins and minuten should be used. White or japanned pins should only be used for double staging specimens, ie where small insects are pinned with minuten, and the latter are inserted into a piece of polyporus, pith, or card through which a larger pin is placed. This larger pin, the staging pin, carries the data labels (see Fig. 15).

Papering

Papering, as mentioned above, is a particularly suitable method of transporting insects with large and delicate wings or legs. Rhopalocera (butterflies), Tipulids (crane-flies), Odonata (dragonflies), and the large winged Neuroptera are usually papered. In humid conditions Orthoptera should be papered rather than layered unless some means of drying the layers is available. Other insects, ie moths, some flies, and larger Hymenoptera, may also be papered in an emergency, but it is not a recommended practice. Paper envelopes may be bought ready-made in a variety of sizes, although many entomologists prefer to make their own. Papers sold by entomological suppliers are usually made from glazene paper, semi-transparent and fairly hard, similar to those used by philatelists;

Fig. 15. Methods of pinning and staging insects. A, Steel points thrust upwards through polyporus and into the insects from beneath (not recommended); B, Steel point; C, Steel point mounted on celluloid; D, Steel point mounted on polyporus; E, Gummed on celluloid triangle; F, Pinned directly on 'continental' pin.

they are square or rectangular with a small closing flap. The rather hard nature of the paper plus the corner angles make it difficult to remove dried and brittle specimens from these packets without damaging them. Although more time-consuming to produce, the folded packets or triangles employed by butterfly collectors are probably the safest and most easily used for all papered insects and a variety of types of paper may be used. Figure 16 shows the sequence of folds required to produce such a packet.

All relevant data should be written on the 'papers' in soft pencil, before insects are placed in them, and if the paper is opaque, some indication given as to the number, type, and fragility of the enclosed specimens. Papered insects may be stored flat in cardboard boxes between layers of cellulose or cotton wadding.

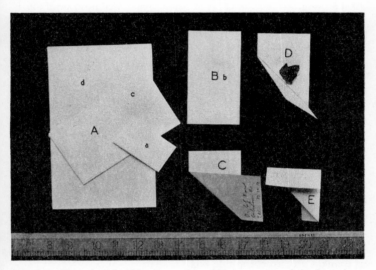

FIG. 16. 'Papering' Lepidoptera. A and B are papers of the four sizes, *a*, *b*, *c* and *d* mentioned in the text. C is a paper, of the size suited to the butterfly, folded and the data written on it. D, The butterfly is then placed on the paper in relation to the fold as shown. The paper is then closed and the ends folded over to prevent the paper opening up. E is the paper after the final foldings.

51

Layering

Layering is the most commonly used and most efficient method of transporting dried insect material from the collecting locality to museum or laboratory. Specimens of the majority of insect orders may be dried and transported in this way. Exceptions are: all larvae, Apterygota, parasites and various soft bodied groups, eg Isoptera, Psocoptera, Zoraptera, Plecoptera, Embioptera, Ephemeroptera and the soft bodied plant-bugs. For further details on preserving these groups, see the sections on special methods for the appropriate Orders.

Cellulose wadding is the most suitable material for layering although any soft tissue may be substituted, eg soft toilet-paper and paper handkerchiefs. Cotton-wool should never be used as it is difficult to disentangle dried insects from the fibres. Cellulose wadding is normally sold in rolls. The thickness of the layer making up the roll varies but it can usually be conveniently sub-divided into layers approximately 2–4 mm ($\frac{1}{16}''$ – $\frac{1}{8}''$) thick. Layers of wadding are cut just larger than the box into which they are to be placed, so that there is a very slight ledge around each layer. Insects from the killing-bottle are placed on the layer and data labels added. The insects should not touch, and it is helpful if larger insects are arranged so that they lie in a life-like position as this reduces the manipulation required when they are relaxed and pinned (Fig. 17). Only insects from one locality should be layered together.

Boxes made of cardboard or wood are most suitable for layering. The lids should not be too tightly fitting unless no further protection is to be given to the contents. Coleoptera are sufficiently robust and unaffected by damp, providing fungicides are added, to be layered in tobacco tins; no other insects should be placed in such receptacles. In temperate regions there is usually no need to dry the layered insects before covering, except where large numbers of very fleshy specimens are layered in one box.

In the humid tropics some attempt should be made to dry each layer before a covering layer is applied (see page 62).

Precautions must be taken against insect pests gaining entrance to the layers. This is most easily done by soaking the inside of the box with a mixture of naphthalene in a suitable solvent (see page 56) before layers are inserted, the solvent evaporates and the cardboard remains impregnated with naphthalene. A few crystals of naphthalene or paradichlorbenzene should also be sprinkled between the layers. This is most easily done if two covering layers of wadding are applied, the second acting as the bottom of the next layer. Each layer of insects is thus enclosed as a discrete unit, which also facilitates handling during the relaxing and mounting processes.

When boxes are full they should be marked on the top with general data, country, collecting period and collector, and then sealed into large polythene bags with a quantity of dry silica-gel to absorb moisture, and crystals of thymol to reduce fungal growths.

Pinned material, particularly specimens on continental pins, is bulky and is liable to damage during transit. Long pinned

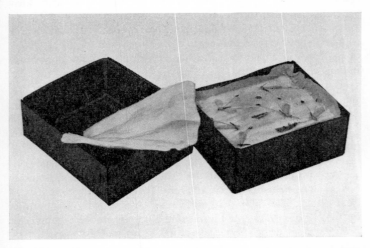

Fig. 17. Packing insects in cellulose wool. The box is almost fully packed. A tissue paper trap has been put into it with a piece of cellulose wool on which the insects have been laid. A second piece of cellulose wool cut to the correct size is shown ready to be put into the box on top of the insects, and on top of which another tray will be placed. The box shown measures 130 × 100 × 50 mm (5 × 4 × 2 inches) approx.

specimens should be kept in store boxes, which are wooden boxes with tightly fitting lids. Both the lid and the bottom, or the bottom alone are covered with cork or suitable artificial substitute. The material used must be sufficiently soft to allow the pins to be inserted easily, but resilient enough to grip the pin securely. Expanded polystyrene, although soft, does not have the latter quality and has an added disadvantage that it is affected by most chemicals used to protect specimens from pest damage. 'Plastazote', a nylon foam, is a most useful substitute for cork and is, in many ways, superior. It is light, grips pins well and is chemically inert.

If double-sided store boxes are preferred, it is important to ensure that the boxes are sufficiently deep, in excess of 85 mm ($3\frac{1}{2}''$), to take continental pins without the pins on the top damaging specimens pinned into the bottom of the box. Single-sided boxes, commonly called 'Schmidt boxes', eliminate this problem and with their generally smaller size, $330 \times 225 \times 55$ mm, (approximately $13'' \times 8'' \times 2''$), are much lighter. They cannot, of course, carry as many specimens as the larger boxes, but when the transporting of materials is a problem, the size of individual units may be of paramount importance.

Micro-pinned material, to save weight and space, is stored in much shallower boxes, the pins inserted into soft cork or a cork preparation called moll, or into substitute nylon foam. In the past small wooden postal boxes have been found most satisfactory for transporting micro-pinned specimens. In recent years plastics have taken over the role of wood, and a variety of shallow plastic containers with tightly fitting lids are available for conversion to insect boxes. The British Museum (Natural History) uses a container of clear plastic, $120 \times 80 \times 20$ mm with a layer of nylon foam in the bottom 10 mm thick (see Figs 18 and 28). There are a number of advantages in using clear plastic, the boxes may be inspected by customs officials without the need to open them, and the condition of the enclosed specimens observed by the collector so that infestations or loose specimens may be removed before serious damage results. Plastic boxes are not as strong as wood and some care must be taken in their handling. They pick up a static electric charge which may be turned to good advantage when pinning and setting micro-lepidoptera (see p. 104), but may be discharged, if inconvenient, by wiping the box with a detergent-soaked cloth. The most serious disadvantage, and one which is inherent in the use of plastic for any entomological storage, is the totally non-absorptive nature of the material. Wood or cardboard containers absorb moisture and even 'dry' insects, ie all specimens that have not been artificially and specifically dried, continue to give off water vapour for many months after they have been killed. **Great care must be taken to dry thoroughly all insects that are pinned or layered into plastic boxes to reduce the slow build up of moisture and subsequent damage due to fungi.**

After drying, which may be accomplished by exposure to the sun or over gentle heat, the plastic boxes may be sealed with waterproof adhesive tape. Wooden boxes should be sealed into polythene bags, or sheeting, of a suitable size, together with a small quantity of paradichlorbenzine or naphthalene, and a quantity of dried silica gel crystals to absorb moisture. Polythene bags may be sealed

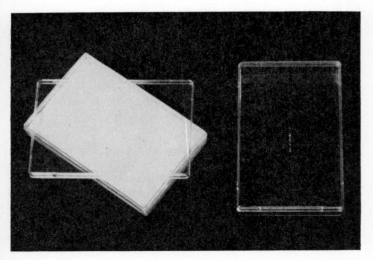

Fig. 18. Clear plastic boxes with a layer of nylon foam for pinning insects.

with adhesive tape or by applying a hot wire to the surface to be bonded. A little practice is required to perfect the technique as the wire must only be hot enough to cause the polythene to melt without burning and distorting.

Fungal and pest preventatives

Where there is any likelihood of fungal growth developing on stored insects, precautions must be taken and fungicides used. For most conditions, excepting the humid tropics (see 62p.) the use of thymol will suffice in combatting fungal growth. Crystals may be added between layers, or in boxes of pinned material, placed in naphtha-cells or wrapped in gauze and pinned securely into the bottom of the box. NOTE: **Thymol should not be used with plastic containers.**

There is a wide range of pests which attack stored insects including mites, museum beetle, psocids and ants. Ants are particularly damaging almost anywhere outside the cool temperate regions and they will cut up and remove piecemeal any insects to which they can gain access. Care must be taken while sun-drying insects to protect them from ants, wasps, and from certain species of flies which lay eggs or larvae onto dead insects. Ants and other crawling insects may be kept from collections by the liberal use of paradichlorbenzene in the packing materials and by standing the legs or supports of any storage surfaces, tables etc, in tins of pyrethrum or paraffin (kerosene). Drying insects may be protected from flying insects by using crystals of paradichlorbenzene. The latter pesticide should not be used in enclosed working areas as like most chemicals of this group, it is toxic to man.

Should a collection show signs of damage by insects or mites it must be treated at once. Application of paradichlorbenzene is usually ineffective once an infestation has occurred, as many of the early stages of the more resistant pest species, eg Dermestid or museum beetles, are difficult to eradicate once established. Apart from chemical fumigation which is only possible under controlled con-ditions and by an expert, a mixture of chemicals of a more pene-trating nature must be used. Such a preparation is Corbett and Pendlebury's mixture or the so-called British Museum mixture (see p. 160 for preparation). This mixture, when the solvent has evaporated, leaves a deposit of naphthalene and creosote in the infested boxes.

Preservation in alcohol

The majority of preservatives for soft bodied insects have ethyl alcohol as a base. Museum specialists and others have, over the years, developed various combinations of alcohol and additives that are particularly useful in preparing specimens of the orders on which they work for future study. Details of these preservatives are given in the sections dealing with the various Orders.

Alcohol is always to be preferred for the preservation of insects that are too delicate, soft bodied or poorly chitinised to withstand desiccation. As a general preservative, 70–80 per cent alcohol should be used for adults and larvae of the majority of orders. Very small and fragile specimens may be stored in less concentrated solutions, as low as 50 per cent, as this lessens distortion.

During transit it is advisable to add a small quantity of glycerine to material in alcohol to ensure that the specimens never completely dry out should leakage occur. If there is the possibility that the tubes with natural corks or loosely fitting plastic stopper may not be inspected, or reach their destination for some weeks, they may be sealed with alcohol-resistant adhesive tape or by coating the cork with a low melting point wax.

Small tubes of specimens in alcohol are most safely and conveniently transported within larger jars or bottles. The tubes of specimens are filled with alcohol and a data label inserted. The label should be wider than the diameter of the tube so that it may be curved around the circumference of the tube. As a result, it is held securely, prevented from moving and damaging the specimens, and may easily be read if the tube is of transparent material.

The label must be written in soft pencil or a permanent indian ink, as certain concentrations of alcohol will dissolve even the most seemingly indelible inks. Ball-point pens should never be used. A small plug of cotton wool is inserted, the tube filled with alcohol and all air bubbles excluded. To ensure the latter condition the fore-finger is placed over the mouth of the tube and it is inverted into the storage jar which is partly filled with alcohol. When the mouth of the tube is below the surface of the alcohol, the fore finger is removed and all air bubbles are thereby excluded. Numbers of tubes may be stored in large storage jars, each layer of tubes supported and cushioned upon layers of cotton wool, which is also used to pack the tubes firmly together before transporting. Any large screw-top jar is suitable for storing tubes providing the neck is of a suitable width in relation to its depth, and it can be securely sealed.

Two important points must be stressed concerning material in alcohol. The first is that alcohol is not suitable for preserving many groups of insects, particularly those groups whose members are identified on scaling and dusting characters or colour characters. Alcohol should never be used for preserving moths and butterflies or for many groups of flies, unless they have been collected for dissection purposes. Discolouration of most insects occurs rapidly in alcohol and subtle differences are lost. Mention should be made of original colouring, if pertinent, on the data labels included with the specimens.

As tissues harden in alcohol and specimens become extremely brittle, care must be taken to remove all air bubbles from the liquid in the tubes and to ensure that labels are sufficiently large. Small labels that are able to move, may cause considerable damage to small or fragile specimens. If a tube is stoppered, other than plugged with cotton wool, the removal of the final small quantity of air as the stopper is inserted may be difficult. The tube may be stoppered while it is completely immersed in alcohol in a suitable large container, or a strong cotton thread be trailed into the tube, the cork inserted and the thread then pulled out. The small channel around the thread where it displaces the stopper, allows the remaining air to escape. Natural cork and rubber are sufficiently resilient to allow a mounted needle to be carefully inserted between them and the stopper to release trapped air.

Formalin

A solution of formaldehyde in water; discolours specimens less quickly than alcohol but has other more important disadvantages. Unless continuously buffered by the addition of Hexamine etc (see

Appendix), formalin breaks down slowly, producing an acidic solution which attacks insect cuticle. It is unpleasant to work with and is not an efficient wetting agent, resulting in a time lag between immersion of the insect in the fluid and the penetration of its tissues. Except in special circumstances, when alcohol is not available or because of fire hazard, formalin should be used only for temporary preservation. The insects so stored should subsequently be transferred to alcohol or washed and dried out if this is required.

Other preserving fluids are advised for specific groups and only general purpose fluids are considered here.

Pampel's fluid

See appendix

Particularly good for the preservation of insects required for further dissection, and for larvae. Large insects should have an incision made in the body wall at a suitable point to facilitate the entry of the preserving fluid into the body cavity. Whenever possible, specimens should be placed into the fluid alive as this improves preservation of the gut and respiratory systems.

Embalming fluid

Very large bodied insects, particularly of the more primitive orders, eg Orthoptera, require rapid drying if they are not to suffer from decomposition and loss of colour. Under humid conditions this is rarely possible and the specimens should be injected with an embalming fluid before the drying process begins. The fluid (see appendix) is applied with a large hypodermic syringe, the needle of which is inserted through the abdomen into the thorax. The embalming fluid is injected as the syringe is slowly withdrawn. Specimens so treated retain their original colours more satisfactorily and are less attractive as food to insect pests.

TRANSPORTING MATERIAL

The correct packing for the safe transport of material is of paramount importance. It is obviously of little consequence that specimens are collected and preserved properly if they are lost through inadequate packing during their final transit to the Museum.

Material in a dried state must be protected against damage due to inexpert or rough handling and boxes of layered or pinned specimens should be packed into wooden or cardboard boxes sufficiently large to allow a thick insulating layer of packing material on all sides (see Fig. 19 (A,B)).

Insects preserved in liquid are more difficult to transport due to the fragility of the containers and the weight of the fluid. Small numbers of stoppered tubes may be sent packed in cardboard boxes, each tube individually sealed and wrapped in paper or cellulose wadding, the boxes packed as for dried material.

Large numbers of small tubes and larger jars are best transported within spirit proof containers of plastic or glass (see Fig. 19 (C)). These larger containers will require the protection of strong wooden or metal crates.

Customs and other difficulties

Specimens in alcohol may require customs clearance depending upon local regulations and enquiries should be made by the collector in advance. Large volumes of alcohol constitute a considerable fire hazard and insurance difficulties may be encountered.

The exporting of natural history specimens is covered by stringent regulations in many countries and prior permission must be gained in such areas.

All parcels, boxes and crates of material should carry clear indications as to the nature of the contents. It is usually only necessary to give general information, eg 'Dried insects', or 'Insects in preservative, for scientific purposes and of no commercial value'. Material sent to the Museum should bear the following address: The Director, British Museum (Natural History), Cromwell Road, London, SW7 5BD, for the attention of the Entomology Department. Containers so marked will not be opened by the British Customs, but sealed and on reaching the Museum, opened under customs surveillance.

This arrangement reduces the risk of damage caused by disturbance of dried materials and subsequent repacking. It should be stressed that *only* those containers addressed to The Director are treated in this manner.

All containers should be marked with notices warning of the fragile

FIG. 19. Packing material for transport in cardboard cartons. A, Two small boxes of pinned material packed in wood-wool. Note that each box is wrapped in paper to prevent its lid opening and thus allowing wood shavings to get amongst the insects. B, Two smaller cartons containing material, packed in cellulose wool or 'papered', in small cardboard boxes. One of the small cartons has been left open to show the small cardboard boxes within. C, Plastic bottles for containing tubes of specimens in alcohol.

nature of the contents. Adhesive labels are available from the Entomology Department of the Museum bearing the following legends: Fragile; Glass, with care; Fragile, Dried Insects for Scientific purpose! (in three languages) for use by persons collecting for the Museum.

SPECIAL TECHNIQUES

Collecting in humid tropics

There are difficulties in applying some of the normal collecting techniques, quite apart from the difficulties due to factors of a purely physical nature such as the debilitating effects of the combination of high temperature and humidity.

For parts of the year rainfall is either very heavy and persistent or occurs regularly at a certain time during each day. On account of the resulting high relative humidity, vegetation has neither time nor opportunity to dry, and so limits the use of the sweep net, as well as making hand netting difficult.

Under humid conditions, and in the absence of artificial heating, extraction by Berlese funnel is made virtually impossible without recourse to chemical extractants (see p. 29).

High relative humidity results in the rapid and persistent growth of fungi. Corrosion and fungal growth provide the majority of the problems encountered by the insect collector. Metal surfaces, unless of a resistant nature, corrode rapidly and most pieces of collecting and other scientific equipment should have their metallic components protected by a film of special grease. The latter contains pesticides and fungicides to prolong its period of effectiveness.

Almost all products of an organic nature will be attacked by fungi and even glass surfaces of lenses etc, may be etched by certain fungal hyphae. Under such conditions, drying and packing insect material is extremely difficult and very stringent precautions must be taken to protect partially dried material from fungal attack. Layered insects must be dried adequately before covering, each layer being exposed to the sun's rays whenever possible or desiccated by other means, in a drying oven if available. Gas or vapour lamps provide sufficient heat

to dry most insects rapidly, but care must be taken not to damage specimens by excessive heating or to distort them by drying too rapidly.

All insect material should be protected when packed by the use of a fungicide of which there are a variety of proprietary brands. Chlorocresol or thymol are useful general purpose crystalline fungicides which do not materially affect the condition of specimens (see appendix). Crystals may be added between layers or wrapped in muslin and pinned into boxes.

If boxes are successfully dried by artificial means, they should be sealed in heavy-duty polythene bags together with crystals of a fungicide, a dehydrating agent, and a pesticide, paradichlorbenzene being suitable.

If it is found to be impossible to dry material satisfactorily, boxes should still be placed in polythene bags with fungicide and pesticide but the bags should not be sealed at once, as it is necessary to inspect the material at intervals for signs of damage. When it becomes necessary to dispatch the collection, the bags may be sealed as above. Whenever possible, such insect material should be transported by the quickest method available and as soon as possible after capture, to subject the specimens to the damp conditions for the minimum time.

Aquatic insects

Examples of aquatic insects occur in nearly all orders either as adults or during the larval stages. It is, therefore, a most important habitat and the majority of collectors will have some need to consider techniques for collecting insects associated with water.

As for any specialised habitat a whole variety of techniques and equipment are available; for the general collector, much of this is unnecessary and only very basic equipment is required.

Collecting equipment

Nets A good net is essential, the variety used depending on the type of habitat to be collected. Generally a strong metal frame is essential to withstand the quite considerable water resistance. There is no advantage in a traditional round frame, and, in fact, it is far more convenient to have the leading edge straight. The net bag material is both a matter of choice and of expense. Bolting silk is best for all but for dredging nets; its cost is prohibitive. Suitable artificial fibres are now available and are considerably less expensive.

For surface collecting, the net should be as light as possible, usually round and with a shallow bag.

For heavy work, dredging through mud, weed or stones, hessian is perfectly adequate. The bag of a water net need not have the depth of more conventional nets (see p. 22) and a depth of greater than 300 mm (12") is rarely required. The length of the net handle depends on the collector and on circumstances, too long a handle, over 2 metres (c6' 6"), is usually totally unwieldy when the net bag is wet.

For collecting in expanses of water too deep or too dangerous to wade, a drag-net is an indispensable piece of equipment. At its simplest, this consists of a heavily weighted frame net, attached by a series of draw strings to a towing rope. The drag-net is thrown as far out into the water area as possible and slowly pulled back to the shore. The frame sinks to the bottom, and when the tow rope is pulled the arrangement of weight and draw strings causes the net to come to rest in a functional position. The bottom fauna is collected as the net is drawn towards the shore-line. Similar nets, but with flotation devices, may be constructed to sample the fauna at various depths.

For collecting surface living insects a much lighter net with a shallow bag is required. A long thin bamboo handle enables the collector to reach species which congregate on the surface far from the water's edge.

Emergence traps are useful for collecting those species of aquatic insects that leave the water as adults either after metamorphosis or to seek further areas of water. The traps consist of a square wire framed net attached to series of floats. Insects emerging come to the surface within the framework of the floats, and fly up towards the light and into the trap where they may be directed into a collecting jar. The size and positioning of the traps depend upon the species to be collected. Long rectangular traps may be positioned on the shore line, partly on the shore and partly floating. In wide but relatively shallow lakes, floating traps are often the only method of capturing those species which have mass emergences far from the shore and ephemeral adult lives. Floating traps, due to their shallow draught, have to be anchored to the shore line or the lake bottom to reduce wind drifting.

Baited underwater traps, on the same design as 'minnow traps', may be used for collecting many of the carrion-feeding species. The trap works on the principle of a small, but easily accessible entry aperture leading into a baited chamber from which insects have difficulty in escaping.

Scoops and sieves [riddles] are designed to sample the bottom fauna and are usually operated from boats. The bottom sample obtained is inspected for insect life in large, shallow, white enamel trays or, alternatively, graded by washing through a nest of sieves. Each fraction may then be sorted separately, and specimens removed by brush, forceps or pipette.

Whenever possible, and where facilities are available, aquatic larvae should be reared to the adult stage. Where rearing is attempted small samples of the larvae and all subsequent stages must be preserved to provide information on the complete life-history.

Light traps Any light source near water is usually sufficient to attract large numbers of aquatic insects, especially during the periods of mass emergence.

A light suspended from a boat or jetty, just above the surface, may be used to lure both surface and subsurface species close enough to enable them to be netted. In warm-temperate and tropical waters, both marine and fresh, totally submerged light traps are often successful. The trap is constructed on the minnow-trap principle with the light source provided by a well insulated, low wattage, bulb powered by a mains source or portable generator depending upon the situation of the trap.

Aquatic habitats

There is a very wide range of aquatic habitats, each requiring specialised collecting methods, and often, equipment. The basic division is between marine and fresh water although the distinction is often of less importance, as far as techniques are concerned, than the velocity or turbulence of the water flow.

Marine and brackish waters The majority of marine and brackish water species are usually associated with the littoral and maritime regions, in the pre-adult stage of their life histories. Extremely few insects are truly marine and few are found in the open oceans. *Halobates* (Hemiptera) is one of the few insects found far from land; these are surface living species easily collected at light.

Littoral rock pools, plant life and mud should all be searched for insect larvae and the varied surfaces for species of Hemiptera, Diptera, Coleoptera and Collembola. Rocks and weed in the splash zone, and drift line detritus, are rich sources of insects, while crevices in weathered rock provide shelter for many species. The flotsam of the drift line should be swept over with a net to collect the easily disturbed species and then subjected to rigorous examination, either a handful at a time on a white sheet or passed through a series of sieves. Each grade may then be inspected or subjected to extraction in a Berlese funnel. The mangrove community in the tropics is of particular interest with a highly specific insect fauna.

Freshwater As stated previously, there is a considerable difference between the various grades of freshwater habitat depending on the rate of water flow.

Still water The type of insect found is directly related to the local geological formations, rock composition and the organic content of the water. Acidic bodies of water or water with a high organic content usually have a smaller fauna than water with a high base or low organic content, though it is none the less interesting.

Flowing water Slow flowing water probably has the richest insect fauna, and provides the greatest variety of habitats, although the fauna is again dependent upon the pH. River estuaries are particularly rich in insect bio-mass, if not in species, and in particularly dry areas, the vegetation at the mouth of a river is often the last to be affected by drought. Fast flowing water is invariably confined to high and rocky areas apart from rivers affected by flash flooding.

66

The latter in flood are very nearly devoid of natural insect life although the debris left after the subsidence is usually very rich in species of Coleoptera (see page 146). After flooding, the marine drift line near estuaries is often a rich source of the larger, more robust species of freshwater insects. The latter are swept down during flooding and thrown up on to the adjacent shores by wave action.

True torrent flow is a relatively inhospitable habitat and the insects found there are usually of a highly specialised form, often well adapted to maintain their hold and dorsoventrally flattened to present the least possible resistance to the water. Fast flowing water is usually rich in larvae of species of the orders, Plecoptera, Ephemeroptera and Trichoptera, as well as specialised species from the majority of the remaining orders. Ordinary collecting methods are difficult to apply to fast flowing streams and the easiest way of collecting in such situations is to remove small rocks and boulders from the stream bed and inspect them on the bank, removing insects with forceps or camel hair brush. In particularly fast water insects may be dislodged before the stones are removed from the water, and it is then a good idea if a wide-mouthed net or fine mesh screen is held or secured downstream from the collecting point. When stones are lifted, or vegetation worked with a net, dislodged insects are swept downstream to the screen where the pressure of water will normally hold them fast until they are collected.

NOTE In tropical and semi-tropical regions the collector should take precautions against various water-borne filarial diseases. When collecting in slow-moving and still waters, particularly in areas close to human habitation, it is imperative that protective clothing (rubber gloves and waterproof foot-wear) is worn. Contact of unprotected skin with the water in such situations should always be avoided.

THE SUPERCLASS HEXAPODA

The Collembola, Protura and Diplura formerly included in the Insecta Apterygota are now usually given class status. All are wingless as a primary condition rather than as a derived secondary state (cf. Phthiraptera and Siphonaptera). The remaining Hexapoda all belong to the class Insecta.

Class and Order **DIPLURA**

see Fig. 20 (A,B)

Usually small and elongate, with long filiform antennae and either a pair of terminal filiform abdominal appendages or a pair of abdominal forceps. Diplura are found in a variety of habitats, under stones, in dead wood, among fallen leaves or in soil.

Class and Order **PROTURA**

see Fig. 20 (C)

Minute, less than 2 mm, white hexapods confined to damp habitats in soil, peat, leaf litter or under stones or bark.

Class and Order **COLLEMBOLA**

see Fig. 20 (E,F)

Although the springtails are among the most abundant and wide spread of Arthropods, they often escape notice as they live pre-

68

dominantly in the soil and humus layer. They are also found in moss, fungi and green vegetation, in rotten wood, under stones, in caves, on snow above the permanent snow-line, on the surface of ponds, in the intertidal seashore zone, and in the nests of termites and ants, nearly always in rather damp conditions. Some species

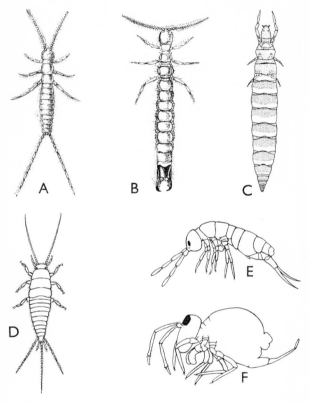

FIG. 20. Examples of the Classes: A, B, Diplura, ×10; A, Campodea and B, Japygidae; C, Protura, ×5; E, F, Collembola, E, ×10, F, ×28; D, the Apterygote order Thysanura, ×2½.

e.g. the Lucerne flea, *Sminthurus viridis* are sometimes present in such numbers as to cause damage to crops.

The larger species, of the above three classes, may be taken individually using an aspirator or camel hair brush which has been dipped in alcohol. A better method is to induce the specimen to enter a small tube which can subsequently be filled with alcohol.

Sweeping may be used to collect species that live on vegetation, and the soil and litter inhabiting forms may be collected by extracting the materials using a Berlese Funnel (see p. 27).

These groups are best killed in 80 or 90 per cent alcohol and stored in the former. The larger specimens should be supported by soft paper to prevent them moving about in the fluid, and care taken to ensure that all the tubes are completely filled with preservative and the air bubbles removed (p. 57).

THE CLASS INSECTA

The Class Insecta is divided into two Subclasses, the Apterygota, which are wingless as a primary condition, and the Pterygota which are either winged or else wingless as a secondary condition.

Subclass **APTERYGOTA**

With the recognition of the Diplura, Protura and Collembola as distinct Classes only one Order, the Thysanura, now remains in the Apterygota.

THYSANURA

Bristletails, silverfish and firebrats

see Fig. 20 (D)

Adults and nymphs are found in the same habitats, under stones, logs and debris, in moss, the dense rooting portions of grass tussocks and other vegetation, in crevices in weathered rocks in the littoral splash zone. Some species are confined to domestic premises.

The same collecting methods may be used as for the Diplura, Protura and Collembola, but care should be exercised to avoid damaging the scaly covering and the long fragile appendages of Thysanura. The best method is to induce them to run into tubes where they may be killed and preserved with 80 per cent alcohol, soft paper being added to prevent movement within the fluid.

Subclass **PTERYGOTA**

Ephemeroptera, Plecoptera, Odonata

These three orders may be considered together from the collector's point of view. The nymphs are nearly all aquatic and the adults, therefore, are usually found close to water, although some species of Odonata may wander far from the water in which they developed.

EPHEMEROPTERA

Mayflies

See Fig. 21 (A)

Nymphs are mainly herbivorous and totally aquatic. The majority of species conceal themselves by burrowing into mud, sand, decaying vegetation or beneath stones on the bottom and even in tunnels in river banks. Species are also found on underwater vegetation and some are free swimming. A number favour swiftly running water, often near water falls where the water is well aerated, and these forms show various structural adaptations for clinging to rocks in rapidly flowing water eg *Heptagenia* and *Prosopistoma* species.

Burrowing species and those on vegetation may be collected by drag nets and scoops, the samples sieved and individuals picked up with forceps or brush (see p. 65); those on or beneath stones, by lifting the stones clear of the water and collecting with forceps and hand net, or in fast flowing water by flushing specimens from their places of concealment into a net or screen held downstream (p. 67).

Adults All mayflies have a dull winged subimaginal form, the dun, lasting only a short period, which can be collected when flying from the water, or when resting prior to the imaginal moult. Due to mass emergences adults may be taken in very large numbers at light, on convenient vertical surfaces near water and in floating traps. The adult males (spinners) often fly in "dancing" swarms around water and can be netted. Light traps should be inspected frequently as the specimens may die due to the heat and distort due to rapid desiccation.

Imagines, subimagines and nymphs are best preserved in 80 per cent alcohol, the normal precautions concerning labels and air bubbles (see p. 57) being taken, as all stages are rather fragile.

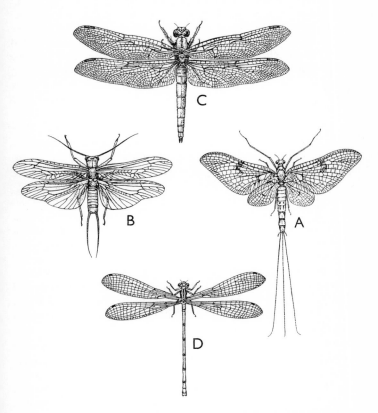

Fig. 21. Examples of the Orders: A, Ephemoptera—Mayfly, ×1; B, Plecoptera—Stonefly, ×¾; C-D, Odonata: C, sub-order Anisoptera—a Dragonfly, ×¾; D, sub-order Zygoptera—a Damselfly, ×1.

73

ODONATA

Dragonflies and damselflies

See Fig. 21 (C,D)

Nymphs Found in a variety of situations, however, with the exception of *Megalagrion oahuense* the nymphs of which live in moist forest floor debris in Hawaii, all the species are aquatic. The majority lie hidden in sand, mud, or among weed and are predaceous upon other aquatic insects, small fish, and larval amphibia. Species will inhabit any body of water and may be collected from stagnant pools to fast flowing streams, including small pools that are held in the leaf bases of Bromeliads and other tropical plants. Species of *Megalagrion* crawl out of water, but confine their activities to within the water film covering stones.

Nymphs may be collected by all the methods suggested for Ephemeroptera and where possible attempts should be made to breed through to the adult a proportion of the larvae taken, retaining cast nymphal skins. The latter and all nymphal stages should be preserved in 80 per cent alcohol.

Adults The majority of species may be taken with a hand net when flying, or amongst vegetation when resting on dull days. Smaller species may be taken by sweeping waterside vegetation. Most species stay near water, often confining their flight to a particular area over which they fly in a regular pattern. This behaviour enables the collector to take some of the most wary and fast flying species, as human or other intruders are briefly but closely inspected by the flying insects. Large, high-flying tropical species may have to be brought down using a small bore shot gun with dust shot cartridges. See appendix 161.

Adult Odonata should be dried as quickly as possible to preserve the body colours and stored in paper envelopes or between layers of cellulose wadding. Freeze drying has been used successfully, but this is not a practicable method for the average collector. Where quick drying facilities are not available the adults should be placed in paper envelopes, alive, and be allowed to die. This allows the contents of the gut to be excreted and lessens the risk of body discolouration after death.

74

PLECOPTERA

Stoneflies

See Fig. 21 (B)

Nymphs Members of the family Perlidae are carnivorous, other stoneflies are herbivorous. All, however, are totally aquatic, and the majority are confined to clear swiftly flowing water. The larval stages may be collected from under stones, in the manner described for Ephemeroptera.

Adults May also be found under stones near the waters edge, or taken by beating or sweeping vegetation near to water.

Adults and nymphs are best preserved in 80 per cent alcohol.

ISOPTERA

Termites

See Fig. 22 (A)–(D)

The termites or 'White ants' are a relatively large group of predominantly tropical and sub-tropical insects. A few species do extend into the warm temperate regions. Isoptera are polymorphic with, initially, winged sexual forms, and worker and soldier castes. Most of the primitive genera have no definite worker caste. The soldier caste is absent from one group of soil feeding termites.

Termites are primarily cellulose feeders, attacking sound or decaying wood, or sometimes on grass or topsoil. It is their predilection for wood and wood products that has resulted in termites becoming classified as major pests.

Typically, termites are rarely found unprotected and away from their nests, only the grass feeders eg *Hodotermes*, and some Indian and Malaysian nasute lichen feeders eg *Hospitalitermes*, habitually forage in the open. Termites easily fall prey to a wide variety of predators, true ants being among their most noted enemies. Many species build elaborate nests or construct covered tunnel ways above ground, both structures acting as useful indicators of their presence in an area.

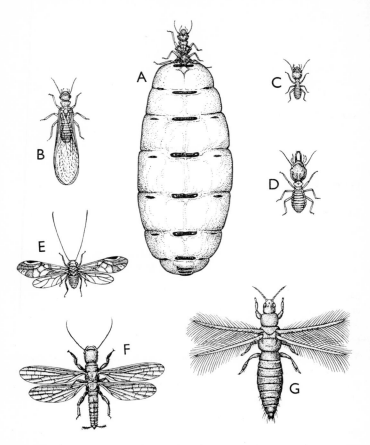

FIG. 22. Examples of the Orders: (A-D), Isoptera (termites), ×1, (E), Psocoptera, (F), Embioptera, ×1½. A, Queen termite; B, Winged sexual form; C, Worker; D, Soldier; E, An exotic Bark-louse, ×2½; G, Thysanoptera—Thrips, ×17½.

The alate reproductives are produced at intervals in the life of the colony, often just preceding or after the first rains of the wet season. It is at these times of mass emergence that the winged forms may be attracted to light, providing of course that their nuptial flight occurs at dusk or during the hours of darkness.

Collecting equipment

The most useful single tool for collecting termites is a heavy mattock with a broad crosswise blade on one side and an axe blade on the back. This can be used for both digging and wood splitting. To transfer actively moving termites to alcohol a pair of 'BB' forceps is best. Some collectors use an aspirator but this tends to damage the more fragile species and some termites give off secretions that may irritate the throat of the collector unless the blow-type pooter is used.

Wherever possible a good sample of all the castes in a nest should be collected, at least ten specimens of each caste allows individual variation to be assessed; the queen and, if recognised, the king should be preserved when found. As many of the larger surface mounds of termites contain a number of nests of species in addition to the original mound building species, it is important to ensure that all the various species are collected. This is made doubly difficult in the very large mounds as considerable force is required to break the mounds open and mixing invariably occurs as the separate chambers and galleries are destroyed. Often the more interesting and rare species make small tunnels in the walls of a mound built by a larger species and those should be looked for carefully.

For convenience of description the termite collecting techniques are described under four arbitary categories based on the position of the nest, or feeding habit.

1 Mound building The most obvious of the termite nests, particularly characteristic of the Ethiopian and Australasian faunas. The mounds, or termitaria, are composed of earth particles mixed with saliva or faecal matter. They are highly variable in form between species, and in size may vary from shallow mounds to structures twenty feet in height. The collector may have to resort to using a pick-axe to break into these mounds although often the inner and subterranean chambers are composed of much softer material. As described above, termites other than the original mound building species may come to use part of the structure, keeping their galleries separate from the host. Such a 'mixed' colony may contain some of the subterranean species, not otherwise encountered.

2 Wholly subterranean Underground nests are built by many species, with little or no surface manifestation of their presence. Many termites building nests of this type are injurious to the roots of grasses, crops and other plants. Digging in areas of visible damage is one method of finding the nests, but rolling over large logs or stones will often disclose their galleries and sometimes nests as well. Many of the smaller soil and litter feeding species will be found in the leaf mould and detritus among tree roots, especially in rain forests in the tropics.

3 Dead wood feeders Often ground nesting species that bore in dry or rotting wood, often into man made structures, telegraph and fence poles, house timbers etc, and do great damage. The presence of the ground nesting species is often indicated by the covered tunnels, made from earth or faecal matter, that they construct from the subterranean galleries to suitable wooden structures above ground, eg wooden houses raised on concrete piles. To collect wood feeding species, dead wood spurs, rotting logs and part buried timbers should be broken open with a stout knife or axe.

4 Arboreal As above, but constructing their nests from comminuted wood. The nests are constructed from particles of wood or bark and attached to the trunk or branches of trees, with tunnels constructed from similar materials radiating from the nest along the surface of the bark. These nests may be broken open with a stout bladed knife, bill-hook or machete.

Termitophiles A great variety of insect species are found in termite nests and galleries, particularly Coleoptera, Hymenoptera and Diptera. Some species are 'true guests', some scavengers, others predators. Whenever they are found, termitophiles should be preserved with their host species.

Preserving All stages and castes of termites are best preserved in 80 per cent alcohol together with relevant data on position in nest, type of nest etc. Colour photographs of the nest or damage done by the species provide useful additional information.

Due to the economic importance of termites extensive collections have been made in the more easily accessible areas of the world. The museum is particularly interested in obtaining material from less well collected areas, namely South and Central America, Australasia and the Pacific Islands.

ORTHOPTERA

Grasshoppers, locusts, crickets, bush-crickets and katydids

See Fig. 23

A large group, over 15 000 described species, of predominantly terrestrial insects found throughout the world, but best represented in the tropics. Although some species, notably the locusts, can fly for long distances, flying ability is often poorly developed and many species are brachypterous or apterous. Some Orthoptera are cavernicolous and others live in burrows; the latter may be nocturnal, living below ground for protection during the day and coming to the surface to feed at night, or predominantly subterranean and making only occasional visits to the surface.

The nymphal stages are usually spent in the same situations as those preferred by the adults. In regions without marked seasonal changes, all stages may often be taken in the same area at the same time. Where areas are subjected to wet and dry, or cold and warm periods, changes in the season will often result in a preponderance of nymphs. Seasonal changes should, therefore, be taken into account when organising visits to a collecting area, as most nymphs are impossible to name in the absence of associated adults. Nymphs with a cuticle that is not completely hardened after a moult should not be collected. Early stage nymphs should be collected only when they can be associated with much older nymphs or, preferably, adults.

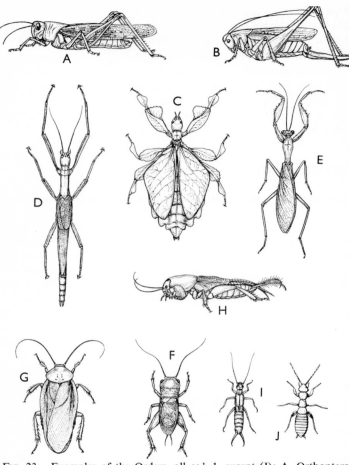

Fig. 23. Examples of the Orders, all ×½–1, except (J): A, Orthoptera, Acrididae—a locust; B, Orthoptera, Tetrigidae—a grouse-locust; C, Phasmida—a leaf-insect; D, Phasmida—a stick-insect; E, Dictyoptera, Mantidae—a praying mantis; F, Orthoptera, Gryllidae—a cricket; G, Dictyoptera, Blattidae—a cockroach; H, Orthoptera, Gryllotalpidae—a mole-cricket; I, Dermaptera—an earwig; J, Zoraptera—*Zorotypus* (×8).

All nymphal stages should be preserved dry.

The majority of adult Orthoptera may be collected individually by stalking and netting them with a standard hand-net or, alternatively, by beating and sweeping them from vegetation. These methods are usually particularly successful for capturing members of the Acridoidea, including grasshoppers, locusts, grouse-locusts and related groups. The Acridoids are generally herbivorous and primarily grass feeders, although some species are confined to feeding on broad-leaved shrubs and trees. Where species rarely leave the topmost branches of trees, or inhabit the forest canopy, it may be necessary to fumigate individual trees with an insecticide smoke canister or pressure spray. Fumigation should only be carried out by someone with experience of the technique and in suitable open areas. After fumigation the treetop vegetation should be shaken, or beaten with long poles, when dead or stunned insects will fall to the ground. Where practicable a large polythene sheet should be placed on the ground under the tree prior to fumigation.

Winged members of the family Tettigoniidae (bush-crickets, long-horned grasshoppers, katydids) live in mixed herbage, particularly bushes and trees, where many are colour camouflaged or simulate leaves. The Gryllacrididae are a predominantly tropical group of tree living species while the Stenopelmatidae and Schizodactylidae have many subterranean forms, some cave dwelling eg, *Dolichopoda palpata* and some well adapted fossorial species eg, genus *Oryctopus*. The majority of the members of these two families are omnivorous, some totally carnivorous. Carnivorous burrowing species may often be caught by enticing them from their burrows using a long stout grass stem. The head of the stem is inserted into the burrow and pushed in as far as the length of the stem will allow. By gently shaking and turning the stem the attention of the predacious insect is gained, it grasps the grass head and may be pulled slowly to the surface. Alternatively the grass may be moved slowly in an out of the hole, when again the insect will follow it to the surface. A broad-bladed knife should be held above and at an angle to the hole. When the insect appears the knife blade can be pushed into the soil, and through the burrow two or three inches inside the mouth, trapping the insect above ground.   Care should be taken as many Orthoptera will bite quite fiercely as a means of defence when picked up.

The majority of burrowing species do visit the surface at certain times mostly at night and should be collected by torch light.   Alternatively they may be trapped using pitfall traps, set above or below the ground.   The latter may be baited with fruit or sugar solutions (treacle, molasses etc) and placed in mammal-runs or covered trenches.   Precautions must be taken to exclude small mammals etc, by covering the traps with a suitable grade of coarse netting. Pitfall traps set in sandy soil eg along river banks, lakesides etc, at night, and baited with 1 per cent formalin solution will often take large numbers of mole-crickets, as well as many other Orthoptera.

Crickets (Gryllidae) of the typical form are usually to be found in concealed places, living in burrows, under logs and stones, in leaf litter and other organic debris.   One group, the Myrmecophilines, are small rounded apterous insects living in ants' nests.   Oecanthines, tree crickets, may be beaten from bushes and trees.   Plant debris of all kinds, leaf litter, flood refuse, rotting logs, farm and even household refuse may be rough sorted to remove the larger pieces and quickly passed through a coarse sieve.   The two grades may then be thrown onto a large white linen or polythene sheet when the various small crickets may be picked up with tube or pooter as they attempt to escape.

Many Orthoptera are attracted to light and this is often a useful supplementary method of collecting them, particularly in the tropics.

All adult Orthoptera should be preserved dry, either in layers of cellulose wadding or in papers.   Due to the fleshy nature of many of the larger species, decomposition and subsequent damage and loss of colour may occur unless specimens are dried rapidly. Wherever possible artificial drying, over a heater or in a drying oven, should be used.   If specimens are sun dried on layers of wadding, they must be protected from ants, wasps, flesh-flies etc (see p. 56) In general they should not be put into alcohol as they then lose much of their colour and make poor specimens when subsequently dried.   If it is essential to use a liquid preservative as a temporary measure, 5 per cent formalin should be used.   In humid conditions papering is preferable to layering although specimens that have been injected with embalming fluid (see p. 59 and p. 161) may be layered without fear of damage. Large numbers of Orthoptera should not be layered in one box, unless partially dried, to prevent a build up of moisture, and subsequent damage by fungi.

PHASMIDA

Stick and leaf-insects

See Fig. 23

This is a group of predominantly tropical insects which, as their common names imply, are well camouflaged in body form and colour to resemble twigs or leaves. The same collecting methods may be used for phasmids as for mantises (p. 84) namely beating. Many stick-insects will fall to the ground when disturbed and care must be taken when approaching vegetation that no part is touched before the beating tray is in position.

Recently moulted nymphs, or adults, with a soft cuticle should not be collected; all other specimens should be preserved dry, in layers of cellulose wadding or papered.

GRYLLOBLATTODEA

A very small group of insects of orthopteroid affinities, known only from western North America, the U.S.S.R. and Japan. They are found under stones at high altitudes and are active at low temperatures.

Best preserved in 80 per cent alcohol.

ZORAPTERA

See Fig. 23 (J)

Minute insects, less than 3 mm long, found under bark, in decaying wood, in humus and other plant debris in all regions of the world except the Palaearctic.

Best preserved in 80 per cent alcohol.

DICTYOPTERA

Cockroaches and praying mantises

See Fig. 23

Insects in this Order are predominantly tropical and warm-temperate in distribution, including some cosmopolitan species of cockroaches associated with domestic premises.

The cockroaches, sub-order Blattaria, are found in a variety of habitats; they may be swept and beaten from all types of vegetation, grasses, bushes, etc, and taken individually from under bark, stones and logs. Many species are found in the tightly packed leaf bases and growing points of palms and other similar situations that their dorso-ventrally flattened body structure allows them to enter. Some burrow in soil and sand while a few species are cavernicolous, eg *Myrmecophilus*. As some of the alate species have a nocturnal flying period, certain cockroach species are attracted to light.

The greatest difficulty is encountered in collecting them, wherever they are found, as under warm conditions they are often capable of very rapid movement over most types of surface. Ground pitfall traps, baited with fruit, bran or carrion, and with the sides dusted with french chalk to prevent escape, may be used to take the ground-running species.

A baiting method described by Hubbell (1956) consists of laying, at night, a long thin trail of oatmeal along cleared paths through vegetation, and inspecting the trail at intervals of about an hour.

Praying mantises, or soothsayers, sub-order Mantodea, are normally restricted to shrubs and trees, on which they are often most convincingly camouflaged, both in colour and form. Mantises are best collected by beating vegetation onto a tray. Considerable beating force is often needed to dislodge them, and it is easier to disturb the vegetation and watch for signs of movement to indicate the position of the well camouflaged species. Some mantises fly readily at night and may be collected around a light, where they often alight to feed on other insects.

Cockroaches and mantises should be preserved dry, either layered in

84

cellulose wadding or placed in papers.   Recently moulted specimens with soft cuticles should not be collected.

DERMAPTERA

Earwigs
See Fig. 23 (I)

Earwigs are a group of about 1400 species, of predominantly tropical distribution.   The majority are omnivorous and, with the exception of the parasitic members, nocturnal, hiding during the day in the soil, under bark and stones and in and under vegetation and debris, coming out at night to feed.   The non-parasitic earwigs may be collected by a variety of methods.   Searching for them during the day in the habitats mentioned above is the most productive.   Special attention should be paid to splitting and breaking up, over a sheet, hollow and rotting stems, tight flower heads, and leaf rosettes of low growing plants.   Friable dung-pats, leaf litter and soil may be graded through a nest of sieves and searched in the manner described for Orthoptera.

The use of baited and unbaited pitfall traps, set at night, is another successful method; the nature of the bait is often immaterial, although some species are apparently attracted to a weak formalin solution.

Nymphs, and a portion of adult material, should be preserved in 80 per cent alcohol.   Adults are best preserved dry between layers of cellulose wadding.

The small and very specialised group of parasitic Dermaptera, the genera *Arixenia* and *Hemimerus* are best preserved in 80 per cent alcohol.   For collecting methods see p. 151.

PSOCOPTERA

Psocids, bark and book-lice
See Fig. 22 (E)

Mainly small terrestrial insects with winged or apterous adults.

Several species are often encountered among accumulations of books and paper, in stored cereal products and even dried insect collections where they may cause considerable damage. Psocids occur naturally in leaf litter and other vegetable detritus, on walls, and the bark of trees, in birds' nests, fungi, algae and lichens. Many species live gregariously under bark, and each colony consisting of nymphs and adults is covered by a canopy of fine silken threads. Psocids may be collected by beating and sweeping foliage, collected individually from bark and walls using an aspirator or a camel hair brush dipped in 80 per cent alcohol, or extracted from litter using a Berlese funnel.

Nymphs are preserved in 80 per cent alcohol. Adults of the scaly winged varieties are preserved dry, on layers of cellulose wadding, the remainder in 80 per cent alcohol.

THYSANOPTERA

Thrips

See Fig. 22 (G)

These are small, elongate insects, between 1·5–10 mm in length, found predominantly in the tropics and sub tropics. Some species feed on leaf or flower tissue and pollen, several being important pests of crops either due to feeding damage or to transmission of virus diseases. Other species feed on fungal hyphae or spores, and a few are predatory on mites and small insects. Many species are found in flowers or the flower heads of grasses, but the majority live under leaves or in leaf buds, under bark on freshly dead trees, or in leaf litter and other debris on the ground. In the tropics thrips commonly cause, and live in, plant galls.

Thrips may be collected by sweeping or beating vegetation over a plastic tray. However, it may be necessary to pick to pieces flower heads and buds by hand, individuals being picked up with a fine brush dipped in alcohol, or with the point of a needle or mounted bristle. Leaf litter and other plant debris, including grass tussocks should be subjected to extraction using a Berlese funnel (see p. 27). Alternatively, plant debris may be passed through a series of sieves and the various graded samples sorted by eye to remove the thrips. Yellow tray water-traps may be used (see p. 36) although this is not usually a particularly successful method for taking thrip species.

For accurate study thrips have to be mounted on microscope slides and for this reason should not be collected into strong alcohol as this makes them rigid and brittle. Weak alcohol, 10 per cent, is probably best, but specimens must be placed in a stronger alcohol after a few days or they will rot. A simpler method is to collect them into 60 per cent alcohol, or even better into a mixture of

60 per cent alcohol	10 parts
glycerine	1 part
acetic acid	1 part

Specimens should be placed in small glass tubes with labels bearing all pertinent data including the name of, and their position on, the host plant.

EMBIOPTERA

Web-spinners

See Fig. 22 (F)

A small group of gregarious insects usually found living in loose colonies in interconnecting silken tubes. Embiids are a world wide, mainly tropical group of insects, some species of which extend into the warm temperate regions. The mass of silken tunnels are usually constructed beneath stones, under bark and among the lower vegetation in dense shaded forest. The silk is produced from tarsal glands by nymphs and adults alike and numbers of both stages are usually found together in one association.

Web-spinners may be collected individually from the web masses wherever they are found, or extracted from litter using sieves. The adults do sometimes leave the webs at night and then can often be swept from low vegetation in the proximity of the web masses. The winged males (the females are apterous) may be taken at light.

Nymphs and adults should be preserved in 80 per cent alcohol.

HEMIPTERA

Plant-bugs, scale-insects, aphids, bed-bugs etc

See Fig. 24

A large and varied group of insects found in a wide variety of habitats. The majority of bugs are phytophagous although some groups are carnivorous and others parasitic. Many bugs act as vectors of plant viruses, and some blood sucking species are responsible for transmitting bird and mammalian diseases, including a number to man.

The Hemiptera is divided into two distinct groups, the totally phytophagous Homoptera and the more varied Heteroptera.

Homoptera

This is a large group of plant feeding insects referred to under a variety of common names: cicadas, lantern-flies, frog-hoppers, leaf-hoppers, greenfly, whitefly, mealy bugs, and scale-insects.

Auchenorrhynchous Homoptera A convenient grouping of families, including the cicadas, various hoppers and lantern-flies, which occur on all types of terrestrial vegetation in a wide range of habitats. Sweeping, beating and light trapping are the main methods of collecting employed for the majority of species in this group. Certain families such as the Delphacidae normally occur at the bases of plants, the latter should be beaten over a tray. Alternatively they may be beaten with a strong, narrow diameter net fitted with a close mesh canvas bag.

Many species are large and brightly coloured and may be collected individually with a net. Cicadas, due to their rapid flight are usually difficult to catch, and it is advisable to attempt their capture in the early morning when they are least active. A dust shot gun may have to be used to bring down some high flying forms from the forest canopy (see p. 161).

Nymphal stages are generally more cryptic than the adults. They may be subterranean, eg Cicadidae and Cixiidae, hidden in frothy masses or serpuliform tubes eg Cercopidae, or camouflaged with ornate waxy growths eg Flatidae.

All specimens should be preserved dry between layers of cellulose wadding, or in papers.

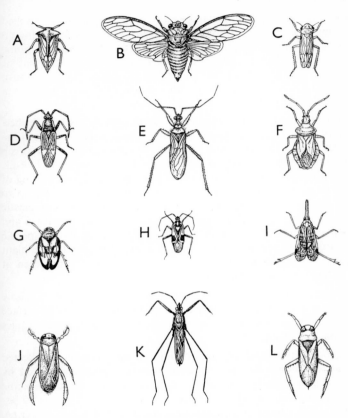

FIG. 24. Examples of the Order Hemiptera, ×¾ to 1¼. A, Membracidae – a devil-hopper; B, Cicadidae – a cicada; C, Jassidae – a leaf-hopper; D, Lygaeidae; E, Reduviidae – an assassin-bug; F Coreidae – a squash-bug; G, Cercopidae – a frog-hopper; H, Capsidae – a plant-bug; I, Fulgoridae – a lantern-fly; J, Corixidae – a boatman; K, Gerridae – a pond-skater; L, Notonectidae – a back-swimmer.

Sternorrhynchous Homoptera A group including the scale-insects, whiteflies and aphids, many species of which are of considerable economic importance.

The Psyllidae (jumping plant-lice) is a family of small, winged insects found mainly on trees and shrubs. Many are free-living on the leaves and young growing shoots of their host plants. Some species form closed galls while others live in pits on the leaf or twig or otherwise distort the leaf, shoot or even root of their host. A few species, particularly in Australia and Africa live under a characteristic scale or test known as a lerp.

Owing to their habit of jumping when disturbed, psyllids are best collected by beating or sweeping, depending upon the height of the vegetation. The specimens can then be removed from the sweep net or beating tray with an aspirator. It is advisable to half-fill the aspirator tube with tissue paper to prevent excessive wetting of the specimens. The material may be kept in this state for up to 24 hours. Galls are usually collected individually into plastic bags and emergent adults should be kept in the bag to harden and develop normal colouration. As most psyllids species are specific to a genus or species of host plant it is useful to identify the plant from which each sample is taken or at least retain a specimen of the host plant for identification.

Trapping techniques can be used to collect psyllids. Yellow tray traps and a mercury vapour lamp shining over a white surface are particularly effective in attracting some species at certain stages in their adult life.

Psyllidae are studied dry, in fluid and on slide mounts. Collected material should be killed in ethyl acetate vapour and stored by layering in cellulose wadding. If large samples are taken some specimens may be collected direct into a mixture of 8 parts 80 per cent ethyl alcohol, 1 part glacial acetic acid and 1 part glycerine. Also small samples may be micro-pinned in the field for double staging.

The Whiteflies (family Aleyrodidae) of generally very small size are found almost invariably on the underside of leaves as nymphs and in the 'pupal' stage. It should be noted that it is at present impossible to identify the adult stage to species, as the most important and satisfactory taxonomic characters are found upon the 'pupal' case. Leaves bearing nymphs and 'pupae' should be collected flat, wrapped in tissue paper, and placed with relevant data into paper envelopes. Light pressure does not cause damage to such material and a number of envelopes may be packed into a box for transporting to the Museum.

Adults which may be swept from vegetation, occur in the same situations as nymphs, and are best stored in 80 per cent alcohol.

Members of Aphidoidea This group is variously known as greenfly, blackfly or plant-lice. The species are found in a variety of situations on plants, some forming colonies on the shoots and leaves, others living inside curled leaves or in galls caused by their presence, while some live below ground on roots. Aphids are often found in association with ants and observations of the latter frequently lead to aphid colonies. Aphids living at soil level on the stem may be covered with an earth shelter constructed by their attendant ants, and looking like soil splashed onto the stem by heavy rain.

As a large proportion of any aphid colony usually consists of immature specimens, the colony should be collected live to allow the young to mature. After removal of predators, mainly small dipterous and neuropterous larvae and their eggs, the colony together with part of the food plant should be placed in a 76×25 mm ($3'' \times 1''$) glass tube with a muslin cover held on by an elastic band. Alternatively if the colony is very large it may be placed in a polythene bag the sides of which are lined with blotting paper to absorb excess moisture. Securing the colony enables winged adults to be collected, an unusual occurrence under natural conditions as they fly from the plant within a few hours of the final moult. Keeping the colonies alive for a few days also enables aphid parasites to mature and emerge and additional information on host and parasite relationships obtained.

Aphids living on the lower leaves are best collected by beating, a large board or tray being placed at soil level.

Other methods of collecting aphids include yellow tray traps for winged adults. Bright yellow trays are almost filled with water to which a few drops of detergent have been added. Flying aphids land in these trays and are trapped in the water. Specimens may be taken straight from the trays to tubes of preserving fluid. The need to monitor aphid populations has resulted in the manufacture of a number of more sophisticated traps mainly working on the suction trap principal. Further information may be obtained from the references given by Heathcote, Palmer & Taylor (1969) and Taylor (1962).

All aphids should be preserved in a mixture of 2 parts 90 per cent alcohol and 1 part lactic acid in small glass tubes, 30 × 6 mm (1¼″ × ¼″) being a suitable size. Full data including the name of the host plant, and the position on the plant should be placed in each tube. Alternatively, in the case of specimens from a colony, a typed or pencilled label bearing a reference number to an entry in a field note book may be used.

Members of the Coccoidea, (coccids, scale insects, mealy bugs,) are generally small insects often showing considerable sexual dimorphism. The females are wingless and in many cases degenerate. In the true Scale insects, family Diaspididae, the females lose their legs after the first moult and the adults secrete smooth wax coverings to produce characteristic scale structure permanently attached to the host plant. Classification is based mainly on the female which varies considerably in shape. Males, when present, emerge in the adult stage with a single pair of wings or may revert to a degenerate wingless insect.

Coccids often form large colonies and are particularly destructive pests of agriculture in the tropics. They feed on the leaves, stems and roots of their host plant and many species are associated with ants. Coccids should be collected by searching the host plant and when found removed together with a portion of plant, as damage may result from detaching them individually. Coccids are best preserved in 80 per cent alcohol.

Heteroptera

Species of the majority of families may be collected by sweeping and beating vegetation, sieving plant refuse or with a light trap.

Certain families however, are found in specialised habitats and require specific collecting techniques.

The Isometopidae, Phloeidae and certain Microphysidae for example occur on bark from which they may be taken with an aspirator or tube. Species of Aradidae are found beneath bark a habitat for which they are admirably suited due to their extreme dorso-ventrally flattened form.

Several families, such as the Schizopteridae, Gelastocoridae, Lygaeidae, Cydnidae and Dipsocoridae occur at ground level either within the soil, under stones or amongst litter or moss, and may be more easily collected by the use of a Berlese Funnel (see p. 27). A petrol operated vacuum sampler, such as the 'D-vac' will extract large numbers of these families from among low-growing herbage. The samples so obtained will need sorting on a white sheet or tray as they will also contain many other insects and much litter.

Species of the family Termitaphididae are restricted to termite galleries while certain Microphysidae and Cydnidae are myrme-cophilous. Members of these families may be collected using the techniques evolved for collecting their host groups (see p. 77 & p. 133).

The parasitic group Cimicidae, including the bed-bug, occurs naturally in the nests of birds and roosts of bats as well as in human dwellings. The other wholly parasitic group, the Polyctenidae, are tropical insects found on bats and may be taken by placing the freshly killed host in a closed container with chloroform when the bugs will leave the fur. Alternatively if the host is living, they may be collected by ruffling the fur and picking off the parasites with fine forceps (see p. 153). **Fingers should be kept out of the way as bats may transmit rabies and in any event they can inflict painful bites.**

Aquatic bugs occur in a variety of habitats and situations. *Halobates* is one of the very few genera of insects closely associated with the sea and may be found far from land on the ocean surface. Species of Gerridae, Veliidae, and Hydrometridae as well as *Halobates* may be collected with a long handled net from the shore or from a boat. *Halobates* is readily attracted to a light suspended close to the water surface.

The truly aquatic bugs, eg families Belostomatidae, Nepidae, Notonectidae and Corixidae may be taken with a water net; the carnivorous or carrion feeding species, may be caught in underwater traps (see p. 65).

Ground-running bugs may be caught using pitfall traps (p. 33) and bugs usually make up a fair proportion of the catch in window-trap catches, although they are represented only by the more actively flying species in Malaise traps.

Light-trapping, as stated previously, is particularly productive, especially in tropical and semi-tropical areas where precautions may have to be taken to prevent the large hard bodied and robust species from damaging the light source (p. 33). It is important to prevent large beetles and moths from entering the trap if delicate species, such as Mirids, are to be collected unharmed.

With the exception of the parasitic Cimicids and Polyctenids which are preserved in 70 per cent alcohol, all Heteroptera should be stored dry between layers of cellulose wadding.

NEUROPTEROID INSECTS

See Fig. 25

This is a convenient grouping of the holometabolous Orders Neuroptera (lacewings, ant-lions etc) including Megaloptera (alderflies, Dobson-flies, snakeflies); Mecoptera (scorpionflies) and Trichoptera (caddisflies). Groups with delicate and weakly flying adults, in which the larval stages are predominantly predacious and in many cases aquatic.

NEUROPTERA – MEGALOPTERA

Alderflies, Dobsonflies

Of world wide distribution, the adults of the alderflies (Sialidae) and Dobson-flies (Corydalidae) are found amongst foliage or on tree

trunks near water, from where they may be netted, swept or beaten.
The aquatic larvae of alderflies are found on the muddy bottoms of

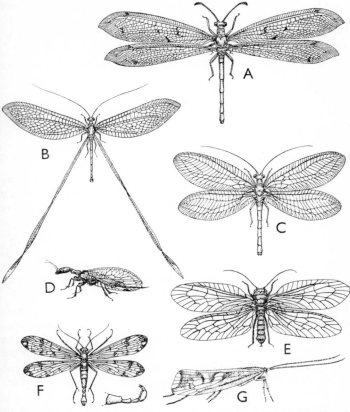

Fig. 25. Examples of the Orders: (A–C), Neuroptera, (D–E), Megaloptera, (F), Mecoptera, and (G), Trichoptera. A, Myrmeleontidae, an ant-lion; B, Nemopteridae; C, Chrysopidae, a green lace-wing fly; D, Raphidiidae, a snake-fly; E, Sialidae – an alder-fly; F, Panorpidae – a scorpion-fly, with inset of apex of abdomen of male from the side; G, Limnephilidae – a caddis-fly. ($\times 1$ to $1\frac{1}{2}$).

ponds and slow moving streams while larvae of Dobson-flies live under stones in fast flowing water. Pupation takes place in the soil, or moss close to the waters edge. Snakeflies (Raphidiidae) are entirely terrestrial in habits, the larval stages are found under bark in wooded areas where they are predacious on other insects. The adults may be taken by beating or sweeping the foliage of trees.

Adults should be preserved dry, pinned, papered or between layers of cellulose wadding. Larvae are best preserved in 80 per cent alcohol.

NEUROPTERA *sensu stricto*

Lacewings, Ant-Lions, etc.

An order of world wide distribution well represented in the tropics and in the southern hemisphere; the larvae of a few species are aquatic. Generally the adults may be taken by beating or sweeping foliage. Many Neuroptera are attracted to light at night and this is a useful method of collecting them, particularly in the tropics. However, some species, most noticeably in the Myrmeleontidae, often do not settle at light, but after an initial inspection of the light source, retire to surrounding vegetation or leave the area completely. Such species should be netted when they first appear.

The moth-like species of the family Ithonidae have subterranean, burrowing larvae and active adults. The latter when their wings are closed, bearing a superficial resemblance to cockroaches and are found in similar places eg dark crevices etc. The larvae of the Sisyridae are unusual among the Neuroptera in having aquatic larvae, feeding on the juices of freshwater sponges. Larvae of the Osmylidae however, may be classified as amphibious, occurring along the edges of streams, in moss or under stones either in or near water. The majority of larvae of species of the family Chrysopidae are predacious upon aphids and other soft bodied plant feeding insects and they should be searched for among aphid colonies. More specialised habitats are frequented by species of Mantispidae, the larvae of which live in the egg sacs of spiders and of Psychopsidae which live under the bark of Eucalyptus trees. The larvae of a number of groups are adapted to feed upon ants and other flightless insects. In the Myrmeleontidae (Ant-lions) the larvae live at the bottom of shallow pits in soft soil and sand, whilst larvae of the Ascalaphidae are found on tree trunks and among stones and leaf litter, etc.

Adults should be preserved dry, larvae in 80 per cent alcohol although it is worthwhile with the more hardy species, eg ant-lions, to preserve only some of the larvae and attempt to rear the remainder to the adult stage.

MECOPTERA

Scorpionflies

A small order of essentially terrestrial and predacious species. The adults are usually found among vegetation and may be collected by netting, sweeping and beating. The larvae live underground. The Boreidae are unusual among the Mecoptera in having wingless adults. The latter are cold-tolerant and adults and larvae may be collected on and amongst moss in the autumn and winter months. Species of *Boreus* are best collected by aspirator and preserved in 80 per cent alcohol. The adults of all other Mecoptera should be preserved dry, the larvae in 80 per cent alcohol.

TRICHOPTERA

Caddisflies

An order in which with very few exceptions the larvae are aquatic and confined to freshwater. The adults are normally found near the water in which they breed. Larvae of only one or two species are found in brackish water and only one is normally terrestrial, living in damp moss around trees. The larvae are found in a variety of aquatic habitats from still to fast running water and may consequently be collected using a number of techniques (see p. 66). The larvae of Trichoptera are of two basic types, the case-building species which, when disturbed retreat into the case, and the free-living, web-spinning species in which a silken web is constructed amongst vegetation or stones. The case-bearing species may be collected with a water net or bottom drag-net, scoop etc. The web-spinning species are more easily collected from their web shelters by removing vegetation and stones from the water and inspecting it in a large white enamel dish. Some web-spinning species when disturbed do not retreat into their webs, but allow themselves to be carried away with the current. Larvae should be preserved in 80 per cent alcohol and where possible, attempts made to rear a proportion of the larvae to the adult stage.

The adults may be taken by beating and sweeping waterside vegetation; some species fly in swarms over water and can be netted. Many species are nocturnal and light trapping is successful at certain seasons.

The larger adults should be preserved dry between layers of cellulose wadding, and smaller specimens and larvae in 80 per cent alcohol.

LEPIDOPTERA

Butterflies and moths

See Figs. 26, 27

Because of the large size of this order, in excess of 150 000 species, and the varied treatment of specimens both before and after their capture, it is convenient when considering collecting and preserving methods, to divide the order into three sections: moths with a wing span of over 30 mm, moths with a wing span of under 30 mm and butterflies. Entomologists wishing to collect Lepidoptera for the British Museum should inform the staff members concerned of their intentions so that more detailed information may be supplied. The Museum already possesses adequate collections of some of the larger moths and butterflies from the more easily accessible areas of the world, and in such areas the collection of special groups or species is often of far greater value.

Moths with a wing span of over 30 mm

Most of the larger moths are nocturnal and the majority of such night flying species are readily attracted by a light source. A commonly used collecting method is to illuminate a white sheet, either spread flat or suspended between two poles (see p. 32). Moths which alight on the sheet can be transferred at once to a killing jar or to pill-boxes; those which do not settle can be netted. Other effective reflecting surfaces include the white walls and verandah of a house,

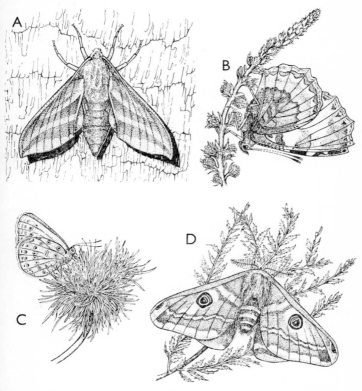

FIG. 26. Examples of the Order Lepidoptera, ×1. A, Sphingidae – the elephant hawk-moth; B, Nymphalidae – the small tortoise-shell butterfly; C, Lycaenidae – the common blue butterfly; D, Saturniidae – the emperor moth.

or a brightly lit bathroom with an open window. Specimens collected individually in this way are usually in much better condition than those captured in a trap. A trap, however, particularly of the semi-portable Robinson or the portable Heath pattern, has the advantage of needing only the minimum of attention once it has been set up. Both traps are designed so that moths attracted to the light source become caught in the body of the trap (see p. 30).

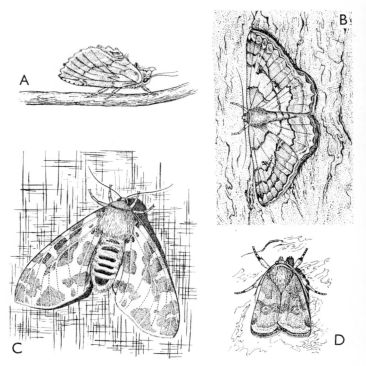

FIG. 27. Examples of the Order Lepidoptera, ×1. A, Notodontidae – the cock's-comb moth; B, Geometridae – the willow beauty; C, Arctiidae – the garden tiger-moth; D, Noctuidae – the lesser broad-bordered yellow under-wing moth.

Captured moths will usually come to rest quickly once inside the trap, but when the number of specimens is large, particularly in the tropics, it may be necessary to use an anaesthetic, eg tetrachlorethane. Crumpled paper or corrugated cardboard, (cardboard egg-boxes being particularly suitable), are placed in the base of the trap and greatly increase the surface area available to the resting moths.

Whichever method of collecting is used, it is important to site the light source so that its rays cover as wide an area as possible. Paths or clearings in woods are preferable to densely forested sites. Weather conditions greatly affect the number of moths attracted to light: the greatest numbers are collected on nights which are windless, overcast, mild and humid. Another factor is the flying time, which varies between species. There are definite waves of activity both in temperate and tropical climates. In the northern temperate regions most moths fly during the period between dusk and midnight, or at dawn, but in the tropics collecting can continue during much of the night.

Sugaring trunks of trees, especially on the edges of woods, or in clearings, may attract some night flying moths. The 'sugar' used is a thick sticky treacle, made from a mixture which may include molasses, black treacle, Barbados sugar, rum and beer. One recipe consists of black treacle with a little 80 per cent alcohol and a few drops of amyl acetate. In the tropics fermenting fruits, such as banana or pineapple, may be smeared on tree trunks. Specimens attracted in this way are best placed in a pill-box for a few hours as they may excrete a sugary liquid if killed immediately after feeding.

The relatively few day flying moths can be netted or boxed in the same way as butterflies and put straight into a killing jar. Zygaenidae can be collected in this way, but are resistant to cyanide fumes unless a puff of tobacco smoke is blown into the jar.

Rearing adults from eggs, larvae or pupae produces good material for preservation providing time is allowed for the insects to harden before killing. The food plant should be searched for larval damage when collecting the early stages as this is often easier to detect than are the larvae. A few sharp taps on the branch are more effective than shaking when trying to dislodge larvae. Many moth larvae pupate in debris on or just below the surface of the ground and careful digging or raking for pupae beneath isolated trees may be rewarding.

Larvae may be reared through to the adult in 'breeding cages' or in 'sleeves' on the host plant. In the 'breeding cages' complete food plants of suitable size may be rooted in flower pots, or the stem of a portion of the plant placed in water in a small container. The bottom of the cage should have a layer of earth for those species that pupate below their food plant. Pupae may also be successfully reared in plastic boxes; care being taken to prevent them from drying out. Suitable apparatus for rearing moths may be bought from dealers in lepidopterists' equipment. When time and conditions allow, larvae should be allowed to develop to maturity on their host plants, and protected from parasites and predators by sleeves of nylon netting.

Storage of adult material presents a problem when moths cannot be set within a few hours. Material that can be set within two or three weeks may be preserved satisfactorily in a relaxed state between very slightly moistened layers of cellulose wadding in an airtight container. A few crystals of chlorocresol should be added as a fungicide. Specimens which cannot be set within this period should be placed in paper envelopes or, preferably, pinned, through the thorax, to facilitate subsequent treatment. Paper envelopes can be bought ready-made, or can be made from smooth, preferably absorbent, paper folded to form a triangular envelope (see p. 50).

Whether specimens are pinned or papered, it is vital, when in the tropics, to inhibit the growth of mould either by using a fungicide or, more rarely, a dehydrating agent such as silica gel in the storage containers. Alternatively the specimens can be placed in the freezing compartment of a refrigerator.

Full data should always accompany the specimens; especially those reared from larvae, when host plant, position on plant, pupating and hatching dates as well as geographical data are of particular importance. Locality data should include references to the nearest large town or village that may be located on reliable modern

102

maps and also the country and state, county or district to avoid confusion arising from common place names.

Moths with a wing span of under 30 mm including Microlepidoptera

Larvae are found in a variety of habitats; the majority associated with growing plants, usually as leaf, stem or root miners, and in fruits or flowers. A number of species are pests of considerable economic importance attacking cultivated crops, boring through heartwood of fruit trees, attacking root tubers, seed heads of cereals or cotton bolls and eating or spoiling stored grain, flour and other dried animal or plant materials. Other more specialised species inhabit plant galls or even live as parasites of scale insects. Many species have specialised to feed on aquatic plants and at least one species has females which swim under water.

Probably the most satisfactory, and in some groups, the only practical way of collecting 'micros' is to collect larvae and rear them through to the adult stage. In some groups, eg the leaf miners, the *only* way to obtain good specimens is to rear them from the mines. When rearing the adult moths care should be taken to preserve the larval skins and the pupal case. The mined leaf may be preserved dry using methods employed for botanical specimens.

Specimens of Microlepidoptera taken from light traps of the Robinson pattern are rarely in a condition suitable for identification and study. The light source for collecting micros should be placed in front of a white sheet or wall and specimens collected singly into individual glass tubes. Wherever possible different types of light source should be tried (see p. 30). In the tropics, where the larger Lepidoptera are abundant and liable to interfere with the collecting of the smaller moths, paraffin lamps are sometimes preferable to mercury vapour lamps.

Beating foliage is useful for disturbing the insects by day, unless the foliage is wet. Specimens may be taken individually in tubes from the beating trays or can be netted if flying. Where beating is impracticable small moths can be forced out of dense low-growing vegetation by the use of smoke; smoke generators as used by bee-keepers have proved successful. Many species of Microlepidoptera fly in the period just before dusk and those that cannot be attracted to light at this time must be collected individually with a net.

Each micro-moth must be collected separately, killed individually and pinned immediately after death. Every specimen should be collected into a small glass tube of appropriate size with a cork stopper. A drop of ethyl acetate is put on the stopper which is re-inserted. Care must be taken to use enough to kill the insect without wetting the side of the tube or the specimen will be damaged; a small drop, that quantity held by a closed pair of forceps, is usually sufficient. Tubes must be well aired after use to drive off any residual ethyl acetate before using them to 'tube' further specimens.

If the tube and captive can be kept cool, the moth may be kept alive in a clean tube until time is available to kill and pin it immediately. Alternatively it should be killed immediately on capture and pinned at the earliest opportunity with a stainless steel micro-pin through the thorax, from the dorsal to the ventral side. Any box with a soft base and tightly fitting lid will do to store the pinned insects. The British Museum uses a transparent plastic box, 120 × 80 × 20 mm, with a 'Plastazote' lining (see p. 55).

When a moth is pinned into this type of container, the wings can be carefully pushed forward (see fig. 28) and the electrostatic charge in the 'Plastozote' base will usually hold them in this position. Should they not remain in position, rubbing the plastozote with the pinning forceps will produce sufficient 'static' charge to secure the wings. It is important when using plastic boxes to treat the lids with an anti-static fluid, liquid detergent will usually suffice, to prevent the wings from springing upwards before the insects are dry. Transparent boxes have many advantages the most important being in the ease with which the contents may be examined by Customs Officers and the collector himself. The boxes when full can be sealed with adhesive tape. Due to the impervious nature of the plastic it may be necessary, in warm humid regions, to partially dry the contents before sealing. The sealed boxes may be wrapped in paper, protected on all sides by wood wool or suitable substitute and packed firmly in a large box for posting.

Data labels, particularly details of the environment, altitude, locality etc should accompany each specimen or the boxes should be fully labelled.

Layering or papering, no matter how carefully done, is not suitable for preserving Microlepidoptera and specimens should never be placed in liquid preservative, except for special collections for morphological studies.

The collection and preservation of specimens of Microlepidoptera is an exacting task and if it is carefully carried out, only relatively few specimens can usually be collected. However, these are infinitely more valuable than large numbers of badly prepared specimens, the majority of which will be quite useless.

'Rhopalocera-Butterflies

The butterflies are a group of perhaps 20 000 species, characteristic

FIG. 28. Microlepidoptera pinned into a 'plastozote' lined transparent plastic box.

of tropical areas, especially in the New World and Oriental regions.

The fauna of the temperate zones is much poorer in species, but nonetheless interesting due to the wide geographical variations exhibited.

Butterflies occur in a very wide range of situations, but are particularly characteristic of humid tropical forests, in which the majority of known species occur.   They may be found at altitudes of up to 7000 m (22 000 ft) and certain species live and breed at a height of 6000 m (18 000 ft) in the Himalayan and Andean ranges.

The great majority of adult butterflies fly by day, although often only actively during specific periods, a few species being crepuscular. No species regularly fly solely at night.

Collecting Adults   As adults, butterflies are especially attracted to flowering plants, from which they take nectar, and to odoriferous pabula of high moisture content such as patches of mud, animal droppings, rotting fruit, sap exudations and carrion.   Advantage may be taken of these habits to trap or bait certain species.   Apart from catching individual specimens with a hand held butterfly or kite net (p. 22), trapping and baiting are the only successful alternative methods for taking the adult stage.

Traps.   The standard butterfly trap (fig. 29), variously attributed in its original form, consists of a net of square or circular cross-section, suspended by tapes at the top and with a base platform, made of wood or suitable material, suspended up to 50 mm (2″) below the net edge.   The net is held open by side tapes or an internal wire frame. Butterflies attracted to the bait placed on the platform, alight on the latter structure and crawl under the edge of the net to reach the bait. After feeding or if disturbed, the butterflies fly up into the top of the net where they are trapped.   Due to the obvious difficulty of inserting a killing bottle into this type of trap, captures are best stunned by 'pinching' (p. 112) through the netting, after which they may be placed in a killing-jar.

The type of bait used depends upon the local conditions and the availability of fruit.   Fermenting banana has been used successfully in Africa (Rydon 1964), although fermenting pineapples, figs, mangoes and guavas are also effective.   Composite artificial bait of fermenting fruit, beer, rum and sugar may be used with considerable success, although there is some evidence that local conditions play a large part in the effectiveness of baits. Traps used in very wet conditions are rarely successful, and where there are excessive amounts of natural fruits, fermenting substances or flowers available, butterflies are obviously less likely to be attracted to the traps.

Rotting animal matter, carrion and dung, especially of carnivores eg leopards, may be used to attract the males of species of certain genera, and human faeces are also attractive to some.

The standard hanging trap (fig. 29) is usually suspended from a convenient support such as a low bough of a tree. A variant of the hanging trap has been designed to capture the low-flying, ground-attending species. The trap works on a similar principle to the hanging trap, and differs only in lacking the base-board, being suspended one or two inches off the ground. Dung or fruit baits are placed under the trap, or the trap may be placed over an area of wet mud or other attraction. Both types of trap should be well secured to minimise wind movements as even the slightest movements may prevent butterflies from gaining entrance.

Traps are apparently most successful in securing tropical and subtropical species of the family Nymphalidae (especially Charaxidae), although species of Satyridae, Nemeobiidae and Libytheidae may also be taken. For further information see Rydon (1964).

The positioning of the traps depends on the sites available, edges of woodland or forests are usually productive, and rides and clearings in wooded areas deserve the collector's attention. Dry scrubland although seemingly poor in numbers of species may be very productive due to the absence of local foodstuffs comparable to the bait in the traps.

Baiting. Baiting is used extensively by lepidopterists, and in the correct circumstances may be used to lure butterflies to a position where they may be easily captured. The composition of the bait should be similar to that used to prime the traps, namely any fermenting organic matter, usually of plant origin. Flowers, fresh fruit and chemical attractants (eg amyl acetate) may also be used and the type of bait should be altered to suit the local fauna and conditions. Baits should be placed on any convenient surface,

FIG. 29. Hanging bait-trap for butterflies.

108

smeared on trees or on the ground in the areas which butterflies frequent.

Many male butterflies appear to be territorial and will attack other males encroaching on their preserve. Advantage may be taken of this habit to collect some of the habitually high flying species of *Papilio*, *Morpho* etc, with lures made from pieces of tin-foil of appropriate colour on a bright blue material. The bright materials are displayed in the area where the high flying species are patrolling and the latter captured when they descend to investigate the apparent intruder. White and yellow feathers, shuttlecocks or pieces of paper may also be used to capture male Pierids. These lures are thrown into the air and the males netted as they follow the object to the ground. Captures must be rapidly made, as the males soon become aware of their error.

Methods of automatic trapping will capture the adult stages of butterflies, but these cannot be recommended as serious techniques and butterflies are usually only taken as a 'bonus' when collecting other insects. Butterflies will be trapped in Malaise and Herting traps, and some species will attend lights at night, although the latter species are probably disturbed from the area local to the light and not actively flying at the time.

High flying species that cannot be attracted to baits or lures present a special problem. To collect such species it may be necessary to fell trees and bring down part of the canopy, thereby inducing the butterflies to descend to feed. Felling should only be used as a last resort, and only in areas of vigorous natural growth, far from habitation. Alternatively the high flying species may be brought down using a shot-gun and dust-shot cartridges. See appendix.

Collecting the pre-imaginal stages The larvae of the majority of butterflies are phytophagous, being largely restricted to specific groups of plants. In two subfamilies of Lycaenids, the Miletinae and the Liphyrinae, and in a few other isolated instances, the larvae are totally carnivorous. Other Lycaenid larvae are associated with ants, either as commensals or as predators of Homoptera or ant larvae. Lycaenids generally, also exhibit preferences for a wide range of food plants, feeding on lichens, fungi, cycads, conifers, and

109

monocotyledons, in addition to the large number associated with dicotyledonous plants.

The Nemeobiidae, apparently, also have diverse feeding habits, but these as yet are poorly known. Species of the families Papilionidae, Pieridae and Libytheidae feed almost solely on characteristic groups of dicotyledons. Among the Nymphalidae in the widest sense, certain prominent subfamilies are largely restricted to dicots, with the Satyrinae, Amathusiinae and the Brassolinae providing a substantial minority group on monocots. No butterflies are known which feed on the Bryophyta while the few species that feed on Pteridophyta and Gymnosperms have apparently evolved from feeding on Angiosperms. Hesperiids feed on a wide variety of plants, both monocots and dicots, and include a number of stem borers, leaf rollers etc.

Collecting the pre-imaginal stages is of particular importance on two counts: much information on the life-histories of butterflies may be gained by the capture and rearing of the early stages through to the mature insect, and the early stages when properly preserved are a valuable aid to the classification of the group. Knowledge of the egg, larva and pupa of butterflies is poor, in relation to what is known of the adult, and there is considerable scope for the interested collector in this field.

Eggs. The eggs of butterflies are in many cases laid on a specific host plant, but equally in other cases this is not true. Eggs may be laid on an inappropriate plant from which the first instar larva has to find a suitable food plant or perish, or the eggs may simply be broadcast at random, laid singly or in small or large batches. Eggs are best secured by enclosing mated gravid females in a rearing cage with the food plant. Species in which the food plant is unknown can only be collected by close observation of a free flying female butterfly as she lays her eggs. Occasionally one or more eggs may be extruded from the ovipositor of females when they are captured or killed.

Larvae. Collecting larvae is most easily done by beating or searching the known food plant. Beating over a tray or sheet of polythene using a heavy stick is probably the most successful method. A sharp tap on a branch or stem dislodges the feeding larvae, and they

110

may be picked up with forceps. **Larvae of unfamiliar species should not be handled due to the danger from urticating spines and hairs.** The larvae may then be removed to a rearing cage when facilities for their care are available, or replaced on the food plant and covered with 'sleeves' of muslin or fine-mesh nylon netting. The sleeves protect the larvae from attack by predators and parasites and also prevent the mature larvae from wandering to find pupation sites. Sleeving is the only really effective method of breeding many species that have such narrow temperature and humidity tolerances that removal to artificial conditions usually proves fatal.

Searching the known food plant or any plant showing signs of feeding activity, usually slight defoliation, rolled or browning leaves is often productive and when larvae are found by this method, and in an undisturbed state, they should be photographed *in situ* before being removed.

When rearing larvae a small percentage of the total should be preserved, in a suitable fluid preservative, at each stage. Colour photographs should be taken and notes made of the colouring, general form, activities and food preferences etc during the development of a species, whenever the collector has the facility to do so.

Many species of Satyridae feed only at night and should be searched for using a red light; normal lights may cause the larvae to drop from their food plant and be lost.

The pupal stage although usually more difficult to find is often relatively easy to keep and rear to the adult, providing certain basic conditions are provided. Pupae should be photographed *in situ* and then carefully removed to a plastic box of suitable size. They should not be allowed to dry out and the humidity in the boxes may be maintained by covering the bottom of the box with a layer of clean damp sand or a layer of blotting paper. Direct spraying of the pupa at intervals, preferably with rain water in the form of a very fine mist, is also recommended, but care must be taken to ensure that the pupa does not become too wet.

When searching for pupae a knowledge of the general habits of the various groups is an advantage. Nymphalids usually pupate freely suspended, head downwards, from a small silk pad on the

111

food plant, except for some Satyrinae which pupate on the ground. The species of Lycaenidae may be found on the food plant or in the case of the commensal and carnivorous species, in the nests of their hosts. Pupae of Pieridae and Papilionidae are generally attached by a silk girdle, in an upright position on the food plant or suitable sheltered support eg tree trunks, etc. Pupae of the Hesperidae may be enclosed in a rough silken cocoon or, when naked, held upright by a silken girdle.

The method of suspension is often of significance in classification and the position and type of suspension should be noted by the collector and if possible a photograph, preferably in colour, taken of the pupa *in situ*.

Killing. Eggs, larvae and pupae may be easily killed by immersing them in the appropriate preserving fluid. Adult butterflies however, are in many cases far more difficult to kill. Adults that are to be preserved in fluid may be killed in it, but specimens that are to be ultimately pinned and set require other techniques.

Killing by pinching the thorax between forefinger and thumb is a method used by many experienced lepidopterists. It has disadvantages, however, as it damages smaller specimens and distorts the thoracic structures that may be important for anatomical studies. Large and robust specimens are difficult to kill outright by pinching, but it is convenient to stun them by this method and then to place them in a killing jar. In this way specimens are cleanly dispatched and with a minimum of damage. Placing specimens directly into killing jars, of whatever type, rarely, except with very small and delicate species, produces rapid quiescence, and specimens may become damaged. Large butterflies are best killed by injecting small quantities of ·880 ammonia into the thorax with a hypodermic syringe. This kills instantly and leaves the specimens relaxed and ready for setting or papering.

Preserving Butterflies that are to be preserved should be stored in papers (see p. 52) between cushioning layers of cellulose wadding in cardboard boxes. It is helpful, to the person who eventually sets the specimens, if the butterfly is papered with its wings held vertically over its back and not in the reversed position that many butterflies take up when dying.

For preserving eggs, larvae, pupae and adults in fluid, fixatives such as Bouin's or Picro-chlor-acetic (see p. 162) should be used whenever possible, and the specimens may be transported in the fixative or removed to Pampel's fluid or 80 per cent alcohol. The study of butterflies has reached a stage where well fixed material of all stages is required for detailed anatomical work. The larvae, pupae and adults should receive a single lateral abdominal cut before preserving to help the penetration of the fixative.

If facilities are available larvae may be preserved by freeze-drying, a process which helps to retain the original colouring. Whatever process of preservation is used, colour photographs should be taken if possible, or detailed notes made of the colouring, before the specimens are preserved. Bionomic notes, as well as the usual data labels, should be made of all stages in the life history, unless the collector is absolutely sure that the life history has previously been well documented.

Knowledge of the butterflies has now reached the stage where general collecting, except in the regions listed below, is most unlikely to produce results of any great interest to the Museum. In the absence of expert guidance or knowledge, it is best to concentrate on the smaller or more dull coloured species, at the same time also obtaining short series, of one or two pairs, of all forms seen in the area.

The need for conservation should always be borne in mind, and it should also be noted that certain butterflies are now protected by law. Included among these species are the following:

LOCALITY	SPECIES
Switzerland	*Parnassius apollo*
Papua, N. Guinea, Solomon Islands	*Ornithoptera allottei*
Papua, N. Guinea	*Ornithoptera alexandrae*
	O. victoriae
	O. chimaera
	O. goliath
	O. paradisea
	O. meridionalis

113

There is a fine of $200 Australian, imposed on persons taking the above 'bird wing' species (*Ornithoptera*), and $20 Australian on persons found with them in their possession.

The Museum is particularly interested in obtaining butterflies, preferably papered adults, from the following areas:

EURASIA-ORIENTAL:

Asia Minor to Afganistan, U.S.S.R., Outer Mongolia, Nepal, Kashmir, Laos, Vietnam, Cambodia, N.E. and S.E. China, Borneo, Sumatra, Philippine Islands and the Pacific Islands.

AFRICA:

Ethopia, Senegal, Niger, Mali, Chad, Central African Republic, Dahomey, Portugese Colonies and the high regions of Southern Africa.

NEW WORLD:

North America, the interior of S. America particularly Venezuela, Bolivia, Paraguay and the Patagonia-Chile region.

Early stages and adults in preservative are required from all areas of the world.

DIPTERA

The two-winged flies, mosquitoes, midges, crane-flies, house-flies etc

See Fig. 30

The two-winged flies, like the Hymenoptera, form an Order in which only a fraction of the smaller species have been collected and described. Due to the considerable medical and veterinary importance of some families of Diptera, most notably the mosquitoes (Culicidae), black-flies (Simuliidae), sand-flies (Phlebotomidae), horse-flies (Tabanidae) and tsetse-flies (Glossinidae), a vast amount of collecting and taxonomic effort has been applied to these families as compared with others. This inequality results in the present very diverse requirements of the Museum taxonomists. For example, early stages including eggs are required by those working on the taxonomy of Culicidae and Simuliidae, while at the other extreme, basic information, even as to the larval habitat, is lacking for whole families.   Flies are found in a very wide range of habitats, in extremes of conditions probably greater than found in most of the other large Orders of insects.   The larvae of some species of Diptera abound in hot springs, petroleum pools and pools so saline as to be completely saturated with salt.   Other species are to be found in

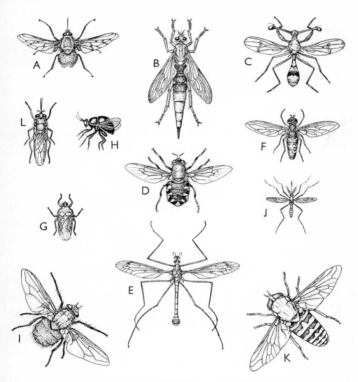

Fig. 30.   Examples of the Order Diptera, approx. nat. size.   A, Bombyliidae – a bee-fly; B, Asilidae – a robber-fly; C, Diopsidae – a stalk-eyed fly; D, Stratiomyiidae – a soldier-fly; E, Tipulidae – a crane-fly; F, Syrphidae – a hover-fly; G, Hippoboscidae – a louse-fly; H, Celyphidae – a beetle-fly; I, Calliphoridae – a large exotic blow-fly; J, Culicidae – a mosquito; K, Tabanidae – a horse-fly; L, Glossinidae – a tse-tse fly.

the branchial chambers of Crustacea, in the nasal sinuses of amphibians and mammals, as internal and as external parasites of insects and vertebrates and even under the pads of the feet of elephants! However, the larvae of the majority of flies are found in more normal habitats, such as soil, wood, plants, various decaying organic matter or fresh water.

Collecting adult Diptera

Most collecting techniques, providing they allow for the delicate nature of the majority of Diptera, will yield results. Hand-netting of the adults in flight, or at rest, is suitable for the larger species, for the delicate crane-flies (Tipulidae) and for the fast flying and extremely wary robber-flies (Asilidae). Predaceous flies such as robber-flies and Empids are often captured with their prey and care must be taken to associate predator and prey correctly. The prey is invariably dropped when the fly is captured and may be recovered from the bottom of the net bag.

Sweep-netting is the most productive method of collecting the majority of Diptera. Sweeping almost any vegetation will result in captures although waterside and shaded hedgerows, and relatively open woodland, provide the greatest number of species. Marshland, mud flats, and grasslands often produce very large catches but of relatively few species. Sweeping ground herbage will result in a completely different fly fauna depending upon the depth and manner of sweeping. Rapid movement by the collector, over the area, with wide shallow sweeps of the net results in the capture of the fast flying species and those that rest on the tips of plants, eg Tipulids, Drosophilids, Muscids, Empids and Pipunculids. Slow, deep sweeping, from just above the feet of the collector produces the more sluggish and weak flying species eg small Nematocera and many Acalypterae. Sometimes collecting with a sweep net and aerial net, one in each hand, and worked with a scissor action, catches both the flying species and those that cling to the vegetation.

Netting, of course, usually fails to collect those species that rarely or never fly. One method of collecting these brachypterous and apterous species from among the lower leaves and branches of

116

plants and on the soil surface is with an aspirator. The aspirator is also invaluable for collecting small Diptera from surfaces over which it is difficult to pass a net, eg fungi, bark of trees, tree wounds, water surfaces and mud and water interfaces. **Where the surface upon which the fly is resting or feeding is unpleasant to the collector, the blow-pooter (see p. 17) should be used. With such pabula as carrion and the nests of birds and mammals, it is imperative, for health reasons, that the blow-pooter is used (p.** 154). **Pooting gravid insects has resulted in myiasis (Hurd 1954).**

Leaf litter sampling As mentioned above many species cannot be captured by conventional means due to peculiarities of habitat or morphology. Flightless species are often found in leaf litter, especially in tropical rain forests and here the litter should be passed through a coarse-grade of sieve to remove large twigs etc, and the resulting material sorted carefully, a little at a time, on a polythene sheet. The same procedure may be applied to friable animal dung, bird and mammal nests, drift line detritus on shores, and the bases of grass-tussocks. Apterous flies are also characteristic of high mountains and small oceanic islands where their condition has perhaps developed in response to difficult conditions, most probably, frequent, strong and persistent winds. In such conditions they are usually cryptic in habit.

Trapping Flies may be trapped by any apparatus that secures the captives after entry into the trap. Although some flies may be taken in baited pitfall traps, especially if a weak solution of formalin is used, and particularly in dry areas, pitfall and window traps are rarely applicable to the collecting of Diptera. Baited fly-traps are productive under the right circumstances (see p. 35). Baits are varied according to the type of fly to be collected. Fruit of any sort, fungi and fermenting sap or sugar solutions will attract (as expected) fruit, flower and fungi feeding species, eg. Drosophilids, Platystomatids, many Muscids, Heleomyzids and Mycetophilids, whereas dung and carrion often attracts not only the dung feeders, Sphaerocerids, some Scatophagids, Sarcophagids, Calliphorids and Muscids but many of the fruit and fungi feeding species as well.

Rotten eggs are particularly attractive as bait to certain Chloropids, and crushed snails to species of Sciomyzidae, Sarcophagidae, Ephydridae and Muscidae, while the fruit flies, Tephritidae and Drosophilidae may be attracted using chemical baits, including many esters eg. amyl acetate.

Malaise traps capture many more specimens of Diptera than of any other Order, usually many times the total of Hymenoptera, another group well represented in the catches. Even among the flies the catch is invariably biased towards certain families although this may be due more to the usual siting of the traps, in rides between dense vegetation areas, than to bias inherent in the apparatus. Depending upon circumstances specimens may be collected into alcohol and pinned and mounted later, or collected dry (see p. 49). Due to the generally fragile nature of Diptera and the tendency of specimens to dry rapidly after death, Dr J F McAlpine of the Entomology Research Institute, Ottawa, has devised an additional piece of apparatus to be fitted to the basic Townes pattern trap. This additional apparatus consists of an extensible tube which is attached to the exit aperture of the trap and leads to a killing or storing container buried in the substratum below the trap (fig. 11). Diptera entering the extensible tube rapidly pass into the buried collecting chamber where they are killed and they are then protected from extremes of temperature, preventing them from drying out and also from 'sweating'. If dichlorvos impregnated strip is used as a killing agent (p. 43), the flies in the chamber become comatose very rapidly, but do not die immediately, further reducing the time between capture, death and the final preparation and preservation of the specimens.

The Herting trap (p. 37) is particularly useful for capturing some of the fast flying and wide ranging species of Diptera. Species of the families Tabanidae and Tachinidae are taken in some numbers, although whether they are actually attracted to the traps or to the black polythene sides, is a matter for conjecture. As in the case of the Malaise trap, Diptera provide a large majority of the insect specimens collected in the Herting trap.

Yellow coloured tray water-traps (p. 36) will capture Diptera as well as Homopterous insects and their use is advised. Captures consist, in the main, of the families Cecidomyiidae, Dolichopodidae, Chloropidae and some genera of Muscidae but in the Arctic 95 per cent of all insects taken are Muscids. Apart from a few specimens attracted by the water surface, the bulk of the remaining species in the catch are usually associated with plants and are presumably attracted to the trap for the same reasons as the plant-bugs. There is a need for considerable experimentation both with the colour and the positioning of the trays to ascertain the most effective type and use of water-traps.

Due to the medical and veterinary importance of some species of biting flies, a number of traps have been devised for specific groups. Many of these traps were originally intended to aid in collecting specimens as an adjunct to a control programme or for population sampling. The unfortunate fact, from a collector's point of view, is that the majority of these specific traps attract and secure female specimens, as the sex which takes a blood meal, and females are often difficult to identify. The traps are only briefly described here, and further information may be obtained from the papers cited.

Carbon dioxide traps consist of a simple trap for flying insects (p. 35) in which a small polythene bag full of solid carbon dioxide, dry ice, is placed. The carbon dioxide gas slowly diffuses through the bag attracting many biting-fly species of the families Culicidae (mosquitoes), Simuliidae (blackflies) and Glossinidae (tsetse) [Bellamy and Reeves (1952) Rennison and Robertson (1959) and Fallis and Smith (1964)].

Tabanidae may be collected with a 'Manitoba horse-fly trap' which consists of a black or red sphere suspended beneath a collecting cone leading to a collecting jar, see Thorsteinson, Bracken and Hanec (1965). Another trap, the Morris trap, also relies upon the principle that many horse-flies and tsetse-flies attack the undersides of their host and then fly up from this position. Dark coloured fabric is stretched over the two long sides of a frame which stands upon four legs. Biting flies are attracted to the frame, fly under the frame and up into the body of the trap where they are directed into a collecting cage, from which they may be secured (Morris 1961).

Sand-fly traps are designed to take these tiny flies in flight at dusk as they emerge from their day time resting places in mammal burrows, cavities in rocky ground, rot holes in trees etc. A sheet of fairly stout paper, minimum size of 100 × 200 mm, is smeared with castor oil and fixed into a cleft stick which is placed, at about sunset, near the resting places of the adults. Next morning the adults are to be found adhering to the paper and may be removed with a needle and preserved in 80 per cent alcohol. Alternatively the oiled paper may be rolled into a tube or supported on a wire and thrust into the mouth of the mammal burrow. Oiled paper traps are not suitable for all conditions as rain or very high humidity thins the oil and lowers the viscosity. In rain-forests sand-flies tend to be too dispersed, flying at various levels and not congregating in micro-habitats.

Light traps of the Robinson and Heath pattern will take certain species of Diptera, but specimens are usually in poor condition and covered in loose moth-scales. However, collecting at a light on a 'moth sheet' (p. 32) is a very satisfactory method of collecting flies, especially in the tropics. During periods of extreme drought there is some evidence that normally diurnal flies may become partially nocturnal. Certainly they are active at night and are attracted to lights in numbers.

Apart from habitually nocturnal biting-flies, particularly Culicids and Phlebotomids, numbers of Ceratopogonids, Tipulids, Pyrgotids, Drosophilids and Calypterates, may also be taken at light. The composition of the catch will of course depend on local climatic conditions and positioning of the light source; the type of light apparently matters less than its intensity and position.

Aquatic stages

Diptera make up a considerable proportion of the aquatic insect biomass, usually in the larval stages; only relatively few species are truly aquatic as adults and even these are in nearly all cases confined to living and feeding on the surface film.

Among higher insects the Diptera have been the most successful colonisers of the marine environment. Adult flies of many families, Tipulidae, Chironomidae, Culicidae, Dolichopodidae, Empididae,

Ephydridae, Canaceidae, Heleomyzidae and Muscidae and others are found between the high and low tide marks, or in marine situations, in creeks and coastal saltings, mangroves etc. They live under large stones or seaweed, but the majority never intentionally become wetted, retreating up the shore in front of the incoming tides. Larvae of species of most of these families are found within this littoral zone, living in algal tissue and fine sand or clinging to rocks just below the water surface. The only truly marine, that is sub marine, insect known belongs to the Chironomid genus *Pontomyia* found in the Pacific Ocean. The female is larviform, and the males swim by using their reduced wings as paddles. The males may be collected underwater at light (see p. 65) or with a tow net; the larvae live in fragile mud tubes on species of *Halophila*, a marine Angiosperm.

Extreme saline conditions not associated with the sea, as found in salt-lakes, are devoid of most insect life with the exception of the families Culicidae and Ephydridae. Brackish water inlets, salt marshes and estuaries, however, usually carry a very large population of Diptera even if the number of species are relatively few.

Freshwater is extremely productive, many families of Diptera having aquatic larvae, and most extreme habitats from torrents to hot springs have special groups of flies associated with them. The majority of adult Diptera associated with fresh water are to be found around the margins living on the mud surfaces or on marginal vegetation from both of which situations they may be taken with aspirator or sweep-net. Care must be taken not to introduce water or wet mud into the aspirator or net. Rushes have a distinctive fly fauna, much of it living at the base of the plants close to, or on, the water surface, or in drier situations on the surface of the mud, While the rushes can be swept to collect the larger and more robust species, the fauna at the base of the rushes can only be taken with an aspirator.

Collecting larval Diptera

Aquatic larvae May be collected from a number of situations, from the stems and roots of water plants, from the mud on the bottom as well as around the margins of water. Apart from the free swimming larvae which may be taken with water nets, the remaining aquatic species must be extracted from the mud and detritus in which they live. Due to the small size of the majority, samples of mud should be washed through a graded series of sieves and each graded sample inspected in a little water in a tray (see p. 65). Attempts should be made to rear any mature larvae and pupae through to the adult stage, after preserving a small proportion of each instar.

Rearing aquatic fly larvae and pupae presents many problems and it is often only possible under laboratory conditions. Specimens of some families however, may be successfully reared in the field. Species of Culicidae and Chironomidae from still and slow running water may be reared from mature larvae and pupae, placed in wide mouthed and shallow containers covered with a fine mesh netting. Adults when hatched should be kept alive for as long as practicable to ensure hardening. Larval and pupal skins should be preserved in 80 per cent alcohol and be clearly labelled with full data plus a reference number. This number should also be attached to the adult specimen. Species of Simuliidae, usually found as larvae in fast flowing water may sometimes be difficult to identify as adults without the earlier stages also being available for study. Mature pupae should be sought under and attached to stones, vegetation etc, in fast flowing streams. The larvae of some Simuliidae and some Chironomidae attach themselves to other insects such as Ephemeroptera and to crabs and prawns with which they have a phoretic relationship. The colour of the pupae is a rough indication of their maturity; pupae become dark brown or black just prior to emergence. The pupae should be dried by placing them on blotting paper and stored individually in glass tubes. Adults usually emerge within hours of drying and they should be left to die in the tubes to give them time to harden. As with all rearing successes care must be taken to associate pupal skin and adult specimens correctly. The adults should be pinned in the field and the pupal skins stored in 80 per cent alcohol or gummed to card mounts and pinned with the appropriate adult.

Rearing adult Diptera from their early stages is a most important method of obtaining information on the life history and complete morphology of the species, and also undamaged specimens providing they are allowed to dry out thoroughly. In the family Culicidae, all stages in the life history are ideally required at the present stage of the taxonomy of the family. Gravid females should be placed in tubes with dampened blotting paper in an attempt to induce laying. As in all rearing, a small proportion of each instar should be preserved in an appropriate fixative.

It is often possible with mature terrestrial and parasitic larvae to induce pupation before the larvae would naturally undergo this stage in its development. This is particularly important in the field where facilities for rearing are invariably primitive.

The parasites of vertebrates, Gasterophilidae, Hypodermatidae, Oestridae etc. are rarely taken as adults and when larvae are removed from the host, the larger third instar larvae should be placed in a container with a layer of damp sand. Under favourable circumstances larvae of many species can be induced to pupate. The dung of hoofed mammals should also be inspected with a view to finding the pupae of gut parasites.

Terrestrial larvae Species of many families eg Agromyzidae, Tephritidae, and Anthomyiidae are associated with plants during their larval development and rearing of the larval stages should be attempted whenever found. Without keeping the host plant alive and under constant surveillance it is difficult to rear young larvae to maturity. It is preferable to collect leaves, stems, roots etc mined by larvae only when the latter are mature or have undergone pupation. The pupae should then be removed carefully and placed in 75 × 25 mm (3″ × 1″) tubes together with all relevant data. The mined leaf or stem is dried and treated as a botanical specimen to provide information on the host plant and the form of leaf mine.

Other and often less specialised plant feeders may be reared from a wide variety of plant materials, fungi providing the food source for many Diptera eg Mycetophilids, Drosophilids and Heleomyzids. The mature fruiting body should be placed into a container on a layer of damp earth or sand. On leaving the fungus mature larva burrow into the substrate to pupate, where they may be left until they hatch. Other valuable sources of Diptera both adults and larvae are leaf litter, rotting wood and compost heaps. Quantities of these materials will if placed in polythene containers produce numbers of adult flies. Alternatively really friable materials such as dung and rotting wood may be passed through a nest of sieves after an initial rough sorting. The graded samples may then be sorted on a dark cloth when various larvae of Xylophagids, Tipulids and Ceratopogonids may be taken from rotting wood, and Muscids, Scatophagids and Sepsids from dung. Carrion also attracts many species. As with all dipterous larvae a proportion of all stages should be preserved before attempting to rear the remainder.

The greatest danger to larval development in rearing from plant material is desiccation and the second most damaging condition is excessive moisture which results in the drowning of the larvae or excessive development of fungi. Large containers are, therefore, usually preferable to small with a layer of sand in the bottom to soak up excess moisture.

Soil inhabiting larvae may be obtained by a variety of methods. Sieving, both wet and dry techniques, is successful (see p. 26 and p. 27) and in soils containing a high percentage of plant debris flotation may be used (see p. 27). Sieving sand may yield puparia of tsetse or of parasitic Diptera that have dropped from their hosts on overhanging vegetation. Due to the need to rear many dipterous larvae to the adult stage before identification is possible, the least harmful methods of flotation are advised. Magnesium sulphate (25 per cent solution) in water is suitable to separate most dipterous larvae and these may then be washed in water, dried by placing them on blotting paper and reared. Glass tubes and jars of appropriate sizes, covered with gauze, and with a screened soil layer, are suitable containers for rearing. Care should be taken not to overcrowd larvae, mix species or introduce larvae unintentionally with the soil.

The method, described by Barnes (1941), for collecting Tipulid larvae using orthodichlorobenzene is redescribed in detail by Brindle (1963) together with a wealth of other information on rearing and collecting Dipterous larvae. In the particular method

124

mentioned a suspension is made of 30 grammes of orthodichloro-benzene in 6 litres of water to which a little detergent has been added. This liquid is poured over a square metre of ground from which all surface vegetation has previously been removed. Tipulid larvae surface from anything up to thirty minutes after application. Where the soil is particularly poorly drained or impervious, a further application may be necessary. Larvae so obtained should be washed immediately in clean water and dried on blotting paper.

Due to the delicate nature of most dipterous larvae and their very narrow humidity tolerances, extraction by Berlese funnel techniques are rarely successful, as most of the smaller larvae die before making their way into the collecting jars.

Some larvae, noticeably of Bibionids and Sciarids may be found by tearing up clumps of grasses, especially in sandy soils. The soil under mosses, especially the Hypnaceae type, on walls etc., often contain Tipulid and Muscid larvae.

Diptera associated as larvae with other animals are usually less easily reared and as such are usually collected purely fortuitously by other entomologists. Syrphidae and Chamaemyiids often hatch from cultures of aphids and coccids kept in polythene bags. Tachi-nids, like Ichneumon-flies, are more often reared by Lepidopterists attempting to produce adult butterflies and moths. Conopids may be reared from parasitised adult social Hymenoptera, the bodies of which are found in the detritus under nests etc. This latter material is also the source of many large Syrphids which are scavengers as larvae in the nest cavity. The nests of birds and mammals are also profitable sources of Dipterous larvae and pupae. Other parasitic groups include the Pyrgotidae, the larvae of which parasitise Coleoptera, mainly Lamellicorns, and also some Diptera. The externally parasitic Dipterous families, Hippoboscidae, Streblidae and Nycteribiidae have been mentioned elsewhere (p. 151). Adult fully winged forms of the families Hippoboscidae and Streblidae may be captured away from their hosts often at light, and many attempt to leave their host when it is captured or killed (see p. 153).

Preserving Diptera

Due to their fragility great care is needed when preserving Diptera and the requirements are varied over the order as a whole. Specimens of the Nematocerous families Tipulidae, Trichoceridae and Ptychopteridae are best preserved in paper triangles or envelopes. Anisopodidae, Bibionidae, Dixidae, Mycetophildiae, Sciaridae are best between layers of cellulose wadding or alternatively papered. Scatopsidae, Cecidomyiidae, Psychodidae should be preserved in 80 per cent alcohol. Chaoboridae, Culicidae, Simuliidae, Thaumalaeidae and Chironomidae should be micro-pinned whenever possible in the field although if this is impracticable layering is an acceptable substitute. Specimens of Ceratopogonidae may be dealt with using any of the above methods depending upon size of specimens and circumstances, but on the whole preserving in alcohol is to be preferred. Phlebotomid sand-flies may be preserved in a drop of Berlese mounting medium in a small vial, (see appendix) or alternatively dry between layers of cellulose wadding.

Large members of the sub-order Brachycera, eg Tabanidae, Stratiomyidae, Asilidae and Bombyliidae should be pinned in the field using a suitable grade of continental pin. Smaller Brachycera should be placed between layers of cellulose wadding although if pinning facilities are not available all Brachycera may be layered.

Members of the Syrphidae and all Calypterate Diptera should be pinned in the field, the type of pin depending on the size of specimen. The larger Syrphidae, Calliphoridae and Tachinidae are pinned through the right side of the thoracic dorsum with a suitable grade of continental pin, smaller species are pinned laterally or dorsally using micro-pins.

Larger Acalypterates and Aschiza should be micro-pinned, either laterally through the wing base, or dorsally to the right side of the mid line. Smaller members of these groups are best layered between cellulose wadding although if long series are taken of particular species a portion should be preserved in 80 per cent alcohol.

Hippoboscids, Streblids and Nycteribiids should always be preserved in 80 per cent alcohol. Wherever practicable dipterous larvae should be killed in hot water (70°C), which expands them fully, and then fixed in Pampels fluid (see p. 162) for at least a week before being transferred to 80 per cent alcohol for storing.

HYMENOPTERA

Bees, wasps, ants, saw-flies

See Fig. 31

This is possibly the largest of the insect Orders; at present rather more than 100 000 described species are known, and a myriad of small parasitic forms await discovery or description. Parasitism of other Arthropods and the development of social nesting behaviour are just two of the interesting adaptations found within the order. Although many methods employed for other orders are also applicable to Hymenoptera, collecting techniques specific to the various large groups, eg Symphyta, Apocrita Parasitica and Aculeata are considered separately below.

Symphyta

Sawflies and wood-wasps with few exceptions are associated with plants, upon which the larvae feed. Flowers, leaves and stems are all attacked by various species, some of which do considerable damage and are pest-species of economic importance. The adults may be taken with aspirator or tube upon their host plants or swept from vegetation in damp and shady places. The larvae exhibit much diversity of habit but the majority live and feed externally on leaves of plants; a few live internally in wood, stems, catkins, fruits, galls and as leaf miners. Wherever possible attempts should be made to rear sawfly larvae to the adult stage as this is often the most successful method of obtaining both biological data and perfect specimens.

It is essential to remember that adult sawflies are very sensitive to climatic conditions and tend to shelter from extremes of temperature and from strong winds. When conditions are right for them, many species may be taken in flight with a hand net. If not killed promptly adults should be kept singly in glass topped pill boxes as many are cannibalistic. These may later be killed by the application of a small drop of ethyl acetate to the cork; specimens

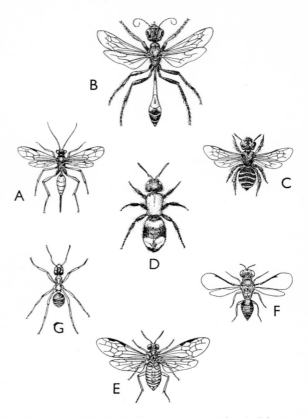

FIG. 31. Examples of the Order Hymenoptera, ×1⅓. A, Ichneumonidae (Ichneumonoidea) – an ichneumon-fly; B, Sphecidae (Sphecoidea) – a sphecoid wasp; C, Andrenidae (Apoidea) – a bee; D, Mutillidae (Vespoidea) – a velvet 'ant'; E, Tenthredinidae (Tenthredinoidea) – a saw-fly; F, Cleonymidae (Chalcidoidea) – *Pedobius* sp., ♀, a chalcid; G, Formicidae (Formicoidea) – an ant.

killed in this manner die in a relaxed condition with mouthparts and genitalia partly extruded.

The true sawflies, super-family Tenthredinoidea, are mostly in evidence from early Spring to high summer in temperate regions, and immediately before or after the rainy season in the tropics.

Larvae are best preserved in 80 per cent alcohol after fixing in Pampel's fluid (see appendix). As cast skins are of value for external morphological studies they should be preserved as well. If time and facilities are available larvae may be 'blown' in the manner adopted for Lepidopterous larvae, but this is unlikely to be a practical proposition in the field. Notes should be made of the larval food plant and of the position of the larva on the plant, together with its colour and patterning during life, and these should accompany the specimen. Photographs of the undisturbed larva or its gall, mine etc provide useful additional information. Adults should always be preserved dry between layers of cellulose wadding.

Apocrita Parasitica

Very large numbers of Hymenoptera are parasitic in the larval stages, the majority parasitising insects, a few other Arthropods and some are gall makers in plants. Hyperparasitism, ie secondary and even tertiary parasitism of the primary parasite, is not uncommon among Hymenoptera and is an added complication and possible source of error as to the true identity of the host. 'Parasitica' is a convenient term covering a group of super-families containing species ranging in size from the Ichneumons (family Ichneumonidae) some of which are in excess of 150 mm in length from head to tip of ovipositor, to the species of the family Mymaridae (fairy-flies) which are among the smallest of insects, some being less than 0·25 mm in length.

Parasitica are most easily collected as adults by sweeping vegetation, or in the case of the larger species by netting individuals. A collecting method has already been described (p. 23) for dealing with insect material in sweep nets, but the following technique has been developed, primarily for the smaller Parasitica, by entomologists in Czechoslovakia. A stout sweep-net is employed vigorously for some minutes in a particularly suitable area. The lower part of the sweep-net bag is attached to the upper portion by a zip fastener and can be closed by means of draw-strings. After thoroughly sweeping over an area of vegetation, the lower portion of the bag is closed and detached. The complete contents are emptied into a sorting box and the bag returned to the net. Small Hymenoptera and other flying insects are attracted to two lighted apertures and by placing suitable grades of mesh over the apertures the larger insects may be excluded. Insects passing through the mesh barrier fly into glass tubes which may be removed at intervals and the insects killed with ethyl acetate vapour. The material remaining in the sorting box consists of pieces of plant material, spiders, insect larvae, ants etc, and may be removed onto a polythene sheet and searched for apterous and brachypterous species. The advantage of this technique is that when only limited time is available for collecting at a particular locality, the collector is able to sweep almost continuously apart from brief interruptions to empty the sweep-net

Biological information is, however, almost totally lacking with specimens collected by sweeping, although it may be possible to suggest the plant on which the parasite's host species are feeding. Rearing adult Parasitica from their hosts is the only certain method of obtaining biological data. Collecting large numbers of larvae and pupae of Lepidoptera, Coleoptera and Diptera and attempting to rear them will invariably provide parasites. It is often possible to recognise parasitised insects by their behaviour, as many parasites produce torpor or a period of unnatural activity in their host, usually in the period just prior to the death of the host. Others may be collected from obviously parasitised, and in many instances moribund, insects from which the pupae of the parasites are visible, either projecting from the host or surrounding it.

As well as larvae, eggs and adults of other insects are frequently parasitised, such as certain bugs and beetles. Neuroptera also at times produce considerable numbers of parasites. Egg-sacs of spiders are often parasitised and adult spiders may have internal parasites.

Some species attacking plants eg gall-wasps (family Cynipidae) provoke a reaction by the plant to the presence of a larva, in the

130

form of gall tissue within which the larva develops. The adults can usually be reared quite easily from galls providing the latter are prevented from drying out. Soft galls which over-winter on leaves are best collected during the late winter, long after they have fallen from the trees. The damp conditions in the leaf litter at the base of the tree provide the correct amount of moisture for the galls to retain their shape and consistency, a difficult condition to simulate. A useful method of collecting galls on leaves is to pinch off the leaf across the two halves of a collecting 'pill-box'. The portion of the leaf is thus kept flat with the gall *in situ*. When this method is employed a complete leaf should also be collected to facilitate identification of the host plant. Hard galls should be sealed into polythene bags and require little attention, although some galls may become too hard for the adults to bite their way out. To overcome this problem the gall-wasps may be induced to emerge prematurely by placing freshly collected galls in a refrigerator for a few weeks and then bringing them into warm surroundings, when the adults will usually emerge. Labels should always bear full data including host-plant and time of collection of the galls. When efforts have been made to induce hatching, this should be fully recorded.

All adult Parasitica should be preserved dry between layers of cellulose wadding. The larger ichneumons may be pinned through the thorax with a suitable size of continental pin if storage facilities are available. Host specimens from which parasites have emerged should be preserved as appropriate for the groups concerned and both specimens must carry the same reference number or be attached to the same pin. Galls should be preserved dry where suitable and notes made upon the position of the gall on the host plant, its consistency when fresh, and its colour, as this is liable to fade when drying. Colour photographs of such galls *in situ* are invaluable.

Apocrita Aculeata

The remaining Hymenoptera are referred to as 'Aculeates' and comprise those groups the layman most commonly associates with the order, namely bees, wasps, ants and allied forms. As adults, most Aculeates may be taken with a hand net, aspirator or tube

In the case of many social forms, males are often found frequenting flowers for only a limited period of the year. Under dry conditions adults of many of the smaller Aculeates may be found in the hollow pithy stems of dried herbaceous plants, their presence in the stem is often indicated by small round entrance holes. A puff of tobacco smoke will usually bring out the occupants of such places.

The larvae of more primitive groups of Aculeates are parasitic in the nests of other Aculeates or on the larvae of other insects, most notably of beetles. Members of the families Scoliidae and Tiphiidae attack larval beetles and ground-nesting Aculeates, and the wingless females may be found when they are pursuing the larval host; the winged males frequent flowers. Mutillids, or velvet ants, have wingless females and are usually found among the bases of plants, under stones, vegetable debris etc, often in dry situations; the winged males are often taken at light.

The solitary wasps and bees

These are included in the superfamilies Pompiloidea, Sphecoidea, Vespoidea and Apoidea, and may be taken on flowers or as they hunt for nesting sites or forage for nesting materials. The nests may be in burrows excavated in bark, soil or sand, or may consits of cells constructed of mud on stems, grasses, trunks of trees or walls of buildings or caves. A number of cells may be constructed in loose colonies by several females, or a single female may produce a large multi-celled structure, each cell containing sufficient food to ensure the complete development of the larva. When completed and stocked, the more conspicuous nests may be removed by the collector to a suitable container and the adults reared. The mud nests must not be allowed to dry out completely as the emerging adults will be unable to bite their way out.

Females of the spider wasps (family Pompilidae) are best collected with a 75×25 mm ($3'' \times 1''$) glass tube as they search among the bases of plants, under stones etc, for the spiders with which they provision larval cells. These insects are very rapid in their movements, and if an attempt is made to net them whilst they are searching they will immediately run down into any available cover. Much useful information on predator and prey associations may be

132

gathered by collecting these wasps when they are carrying their prey. Some species that prey on funnel-web spiders do not remove the spider to a prepared cell, but after paralysing it lay an egg on the host *in situ*; the spider may be found with its attendant larva, on the web at the base of the funnel.

The social Hymenoptera (ants, bees and wasps)

Ants Superfamily Formicoidea, are a very numerous group best represented in the tropics but widely distributed throughout the world. The majority of species are social, with the exception of certain 'parasitic' species found living in the nests of other ants. Nests are found in a variety of places, usually under stones, bark or in rotting logs. Many ants are subterranean and some species live in quite close association with termites, often constructing parallel galleries with those of the termites and entering at intervals to prey on them. Some species live inside plant stems and in a few cases in galls, which are apparently produced in response to the ants' presence. Because of their ferocity the ants provide the plants with protection against herviborous insects, mammals etc. Ant associations with aphids (p. 91) and lepidopterous larvae (p. 109) are, apparently, advantageous to both species, and where such associations are found both symbionts should be preserved in the same tube. Other insects, including many species of beetle, fly, springtail etc, are also found in ants' nests and these inquilines should always be preserved, preferably in the same tube as the ant host or at least associated with the host by the same code on the labels.

The larger ants may be taken singly with the fingers, except for those species which have powerful stings or mandibles, when forceps should be used. Smaller ants are most easily picked up by touching the specimen with a pair of forceps or brush dipped in 70 per cent alcohol. The ant is held by the surface tension of the liquid and can be transferred to a tube of 70 per cent alcohol in which it is killed and preserved.

By moving around in an area and picking up single ants as they are found, a good general collection of the most common species in an area may be made. Separate tubes should be used for each sample taken. Specific habitats should also be investigated, eg under stones. Rotten logs may be minutely dissected, and leaf litter and other plant debris sieved and searched. The finer debris from rotten logs and litter may then be subjected to funnel extraction (see p. 27). All the ants from a single location should be placed in one tube and in this way knowledge of the associations of ant species and their habitat may be built up.

Fumigation is particularly useful in the tropics for sampling the diverse and abundant ant fauna of the forest canopies. The area around the tree or trees to be sampled is cleared of vegetation and covered with a polythene or cotton sheet. Pyrethrum, in suspension, is then sprayed into the canopy or upper foliage using a hand or machine operated mist blower. After the pyrethrum has had time to take effect, the tree is shaken if small, or the branches beaten, and the now moribund or dead insects fall on to the sheet below.

Specimens are collected from the sheet and placed in 70 per cent alcohol. Full data including the height and species of tree should be included with the collection. Care must be taken not to leave the ground sheets unattended for long before gathering the specimens, or ground-foraging and scavenging ants will attempt to remove the bodies of the canopy insects and themselves succumb to the pyrethrum. These additional specimens will, of course, invalidate the data. Unfortunately the very small species often adhere to the leaves in a thin film of the pyrethrum carrier and do not fall when the branches are beaten.

Ants may be taken in numbers in baited ground traps and even unbaited fall traps, often to the detriment of other captured insects. Most of the baits used for other insects will attract ants, but unless precautions are taken to ensure their capture and death many ants will enter and leave the traps at will, climbing on surfaces that most other insects find impossible.

Sticky traps, consisting of a board or piece of cardboard coated with suitable gum and suspended from the branches of a tree, will take species of ants and alate forms of a number of species not normally taken in other traps. Sticky gums are often difficult to buy, but tree-banding compounds are usually suitable. The trapped ants may be removed from the boards with an organic solvent, such as acetone, and then transferred to alcohol. The formula for the commercial gum 'Tacky-tack' is given (Appendix 1) with the permission of Craven Chemicals, Evesham.

Alate forms are frequently taken at light, often in very large numbers. Unfortunately, males of many species are virtually impossible to identify to species if not taken in association with workers or queens.

In searching for inquilines or parasitic species the nests of the host-species should be located and thoroughly investigated. The samples of inquilines or social parasites should always be accompanied by a few individuals of the host-species in the tube.

The rarely found females of Driver ants may be obtained by trailing a column until a temporary nest is found and then soaking the nest with petrol, which rapidly kills the workers. The queen may be found by carefully searching through the colony, and digging into the soil below the nest if necessary.

Social bees and wasps Only a minority of the species in the superfamilies Apoidea and Vespoidea exhibit social nesting behaviour, but these species are of considerable interest and importance. The communal nests may be found in a variety of situations. Some species of the genera *Bombus* and *Vespula* nest in holes in the ground. Small mammal burrows, cavities under tree roots etc, are enlarged to accomodate the nest structure. Other wasps and bees nest in holes in trees, either in sound growing timber or fallen rotting logs. Nests are also constructed around branches and stems of trees and bushes, or hanging from convenient surfaces under rocks, from large leaves or branches, etc. Although most nests are globular in form some are flat and attached firmly to walls or to the trunks of trees.

To enable studies to be made of variations in form of individuals within a caste, and of the proportions of the castes usually present in a nest, some complete nests including all the occupants must be collected. Where this is impossible individual specimens of the worker caste may be collected in the area around a large nest. Bees may be taken when visiting flowers, and wasps when hunting for prey, or close to the nest on the flight path to the entrance hole of the nest. In many cases, particularly with wasps, these individual specimens are of only limited value but nevertheless they often provide the only captured representatives and may still be of interest to the museum taxonomist; similarly empty nests with no associated insects provide little information.

Collecting complete nests is often a difficult and dangerous task. Many bees and wasps are extremely aggressive and, quite understandably, will attack any unfamiliar object approaching the nest. Before attempting to collect the larger nests of wasps and bees, especially in the tropics, the collector should don protective clothing of hat with head veil, gloves and long coat. The ankles and wrists should also be protected and the clothing secured against entry of the attacking insects at these points. With experience the collector will be able to predict the degree of aggressive behaviour likely to be shown by the various species of social Hymenoptera, and in many cases much of the protective clothing can be discarded.

Easily accessible hanging nests and small nests on twigs or leaves may be taken with comparative ease. After carefully approaching the nests they should be rapidly dislodged by either cutting through the nest supports with a sharp knife or through the supporting leaves or branches with secateurs. The complete nest may then be dropped into a large polythene bag containing an open cyanide jar or ball of cotton wool soaked in ethyl acetate. The mouth of the bag should be immediately closed by gathering and folding the top 50–100 mm down before securing with wire or string. If the top is not folded down tightly wasps will often force their way out through the folds of the bag mouth. If the above procedure is carried out rapidly the majority of the wasps within the nest will be captured. To provide additional information on the population of the nest, etc an attempt should be made to capture the insects away foraging at the time of the nest's removal. These will usually congregate during the following 24 hours close to the original site of the nest or on a convenient structure nearby, where they may be taken with a net. Dusk or dawn are probably the best times of day to collect nests as the majority of the occupants are within. Richards (1951) considers 06.00 hours the best time for collecting nests in South America. Nests in holes in the ground or trees may be taken by introducing a killing agent into the hole and plugging the entrances. Again it is advisable to carry out this operation at dawn or dusk to avoid leaving too many insects outside the nest. After the insects are killed the nest chambers may then be opened and the complete nest removed.

It is very difficult to collect nests firmly attached to walls or branches or trunks of trees. It is necessary to attempt to cover the nest with a sheet of polythene, secure it tightly, and introduce a killing agent into the nests. After a suitable period has elapsed the nest may be cut open and the contents removed. Nests high in trees are probably best secured by cutting them free with a pruning knife on a long pole, and dropping the nest and contents into a deep net also held on a long pole. The net mouth may be twisted over once the nest is inside, to reduce the ease with which the wasps escape while it is lowered to the ground. This method is rarely fully satisfactory and many workers will escape before they can be anaesthetised.

Once a nest has been secured and the adult insects killed it is necessary to cut it open so that all the adults and samples of immature stages may be taken. Small nests may be preserved whole in alcohol, but larger nests, especially if constructed of wasp paper or wax, may not be suitable for preservation. In such situations the nest should be photographed before being opened and notes made of the various immature stages present and number of cells and cell layers. A sample of each stage should be preserved in 70 per cent alcohol together with the majority of the adults. A number of adults should be preserved dry between layers of cellulose wadding.

Many nests contain inquilines and parasites, both Hymenopterous and of other orders. Whenever possible insects associated with the nest should be preserved along with the nest contents. If the wasps and bees have been killed quickly and the nest area is opened rapidly it is often possible to rear many of the scavenging larvae. Many larvae are found in the detritus in the nest, or below it in the case of nests in underground burrows, and many rare or unusual insects may be taken in this way.

General collecting methods applicable to all groups of Hymenoptera

Malaise trap This trap (p. 38) was originally designed by Malaise to facilitate the collecting of Hymenoptera. Symphyta and Parasitica among Hymenoptera usually predominate in the catch, with only the smaller species of winged Aculeates represented.

Light-trapping Many winged males of groups of Hymenoptera otherwise rarely encountered may be taken at light. Males of Mutillids and Tiphiids and the flying castes of ants are often attracted to light in large numbers. Due to the difficulty in identifying the males of ants it is important to try and associate the winged males and females wherever possible.

Funnel extraction Both wet and dry extraction techniques (see p. 26 and p. 27) are useful methods of obtaining the very small species of ants and other brachypterous and apterous Hymenoptera. Damp leaf mould, rotten wood, friable soil and dung should all be passed through a coarse sieve before being subjected to extraction. Many species of ant are found at considerable depths in the soil and whenever the opportunity arises, eg during the digging of ditches, foundations etc, these sub-surface soils should be investigated.

Other traps Pitfall traps will capture many of the ground-running species of Hymenoptera. The majority of ground traps however are made less effective by the presence in the area of large numbers of ants, resulting in loss of the bait and of previously collected insects. Traps baited with a very dilute formalin mixture effectively overcome this problem.

Sugar-based baits of the types described for use in luring Lepidoptera (p. 101) will attract some bees, wasps and ants when applied to suitable surfaces. Bees and wasps may also be taken in the traps designed for capturing small flying insects (p. 35) if the entrance apertures are sufficiently large.

Yellow water tray traps (p. 36) are often effective in capturing small parasitica.

Trap nesting A technique perfected by F Balfour Browne (1925) may be employed to obtain the immature stages and prey of many

138

species of solitary wasps and bees. In its simplest form hollow sticks or split pith of various sizes are bound together in bundles and left in suitable areas to be discovered by prospective tenants. The bundles are left undisturbed for at least a week, when they are collected up and either the contents are removed and preserved in 70 per cent alcohol, or an attempt is made to rear the immature stages through to the adult.

A more elaborate method of holding the nest sticks and the techniques for rearing the immature stages are given by F Balfour Browne (1925) (a convenient precis appears in the *Hymenopterists' Handbook* p. 84). Short lengths of elder are bored and plugged at one end and placed in ventilator bricks; numbers of bricks may be built up into a 'bee wall'. By this method the elder stems are conveniently spaced allowing for the occupied and completed nests to be removed without disturbing the surrounding stems. A similar holder may be constructed from a flat board with holes drilled to take the pithy stems. Alternatively pieces of dowelling may be used in the board if they are first hollowed and then split longitudinally, the halves being bound together with tape or elastic bands, (fig. 32). Plastic drinking straws may also be used. Other methods of trap nesting are described by Krombein (1967).

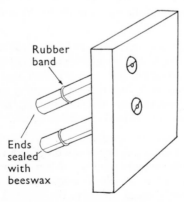

Fig. 32. Levin's trap nest for solitary Hymenoptera.

139

COLEOPTERA

Beetles

See Fig. 33

This is the largest order of insects, with an estimated 250 000 species described. As one would expect with such a large and diverse order, beetles are found in almost every conceivable habitat and a wide variety of collecting techniques are used to catch them. Almost all the techniques considered in the first general part of this guide may be used to collect Coleoptera although some are, of course, far more successful than others.

Before considering the techniques in detail there are a few general remarks to be made which cover the group as a whole. Many species feign death when disturbed and it is therefore necessary to wait for a few minutes, up to ten in some cases, before discarding any sweepings, beatings or sifted materials. Species living amongst vegetation may drop to the ground as the collector approaches and considerable care must be taken not to disturb vegetation before the beating tray is in position or to allow one's shadow to fall on the insects.

In comparison with other insects some species of beetles are difficult to kill and unless left in the killing bottle for some time will recover hours later.

Some of the techniques described below may cause damage to the habitat, and although this is usually only of a temporary nature, they should be carried out only over a limited area at any one site. Before such action as felling trees or trampling stream banks are undertaken, all possible consequences should be considered and enquiries made as to local land ownership or use.

With the exception of the relatively few species of beetle that are capable of withstanding very dry conditions, beetles in common with most insects prefer moist habitats. When the moisture content of detritus, dung, refuse, closely growing vegetation, etc falls below an acceptable level, beetles will leave the material to seek damper conditions elsewhere.

Collecting Coleoptera

Beating A beating tray or a sheet of opaque polythene is placed under the tree or bush and the branches beaten with a heavy stick. Burned or scorched trees and dead wood should be included in the search. In temperate regions certain types of tree are usually more productive than others, eg elms, oaks, willows and thorn. Beating conifers will yield bud feeding species, and Coccinellids associated with aphids and scale insects. Taking advantage of the tendency of beetles to drop from vegetation when disturbed, beating the trunks of large trees may cause beetles to fall from the crown.

A sweep net is often useful for low vegetation, bushes etc. where a beating tray is difficult to use. Branches or individual bunches of blossom or leaves may be enclosed in the net before beating to ensure that the beetles fall into the bottom of the net bag rather than scattering or taking flight. This latter action is particularly noticeable in species frequenting blossoms and large flower heads. Should these beetles be allowed to fall any distance through the air they will instinctively take flight and be lost to the collector.

Sweeping The technique of sweeping differs slightly from that used for many flying insects. Firm continuous strokes are required without a pause at the end of a sweep and the lower edge of the net should lead slightly ie, the net mouth tilted backwards. This tilting of the net mouth is necessary to catch the many beetles that fall from vegetation as it is disturbed.

Grass and generally low growing herbage, dry and dead as well as living, may be swept with a sweep net. Results obtained are usually closely correlated with the methods used and the time of day or season, weather and the position and depth of the net in the vegetation during sweeping. Notes should be made of predominant species of plants in mixed vegetation, and of any pure stands of plants swept.

Sifting Vegetable debris of all kinds including leaf litter, heaps of cut vegetation, leaf rosettes at the bases of plants, reed refuse, flood refuse caught and left on river banks, drift-line weed and other debris on the sea-shore, large flower heads, rotting timber, garden compost heaps and fairly dry and friable dung should all be broken

141

up and passed through a coarse-graded sieve. The graded debris may then be bagged for transporting to a suitable work area where

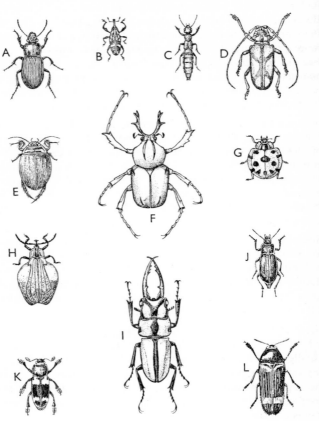

Fig. 33. Examples of the Order Coleoptera, ×1. A, Carabidae – a ground beetle; B, Curculionidae – a weevil; C, Staphylonidae – a devil's coach horse beetle; D, Cerambycidae – a long-horned beetle; E, Dytiscidae – a water beetle; F, Scarabaeidae – a chafer; G, Coccinellidae – a large ladybird; H, Lycidae – a lycid beetle; I, Lucanidae – a stag-beetle; J, Tenebrionidae; K, Erotylidae; L, Buprestidae – a jewel-beetle.

it should be sorted as soon as possible. Small quantities of the sifted litter are spread on a polythene sheet or in a shallow bowl and the beetles removed with a tube pooter or brush. Tussocks of grass and sedge are particularly productive and should be searched whenever the opportunity arises. The tussocks should be cut off at ground level to exclude as much soil as possible and broken up over a sheet. The first grade of debris should then be coarse sifted and dealt with as described above. A handy tool for cutting the tussocks is made from a fine-toothed saw blade set at an angle of nearly 90° in a wooden handle. The angle of the blade enables the collector to cut the base of the tussock without the surrounding vegetation interfering with his hand movements. The very finest debris from plant sifting should be subjected to extraction in a Berlese funnel so that the smallest beetles may be collected. In wet marshy areas reeds and rushes should be pulled up and the stems and roots investigated. Mosses may be squeezed dry and shredded, and reed bases in dried-up ponds and streams treated in a similar manner. The moist and leafy mosses that grow into large masses such as *Polytricum* are the most productive, while the closely-knit short mosses such as the Hypnaceae rarely contain beetles.

Not only should friable dung be broken up and sifted, but the soil under it should also be collected and subjected to the same treatment. In dry climates, wherever it is practicable, dung should be inspected as soon as possible after it is deposited as many species are only attracted to it while the moisture content is high. Fresh and dry carrion should be treated in a similar manner to dung, the dried carcasses being broken up, or beaten, over a sheet, and, in addition, the soil under the corpse searched for beetles. In both dung and carrion there is a distinct succession of species until the nidus is completely consumed or desiccated.

Rotting material in large leaf axils and leaf bases and fungal fruiting bodies are reliable sources of larval and adult beetles; some larger and more robust fungi, eg *Polyporus*, may be beaten *in situ*. Bark should be removed from dead timber and, where possible, the complete log should be broken up to find longicorn and lamellicorn species. Seed pods and fruits may be cut up as they often contain Bruchid and weevil species.

Beetles are often found as scavengers and predators in the nests of birds and mammals, and as inquilines and predators in the nests of insects. Ant and termite nests, especially in the tropics, should be searched for inquilines (usually species of the family Staphylinidae) many of which bear a superficial resemblance to their hosts. Certain beetles, again mainly Staphylinidae, are found running with army ants, *Dorylus* (see p. 133 for information on collecting the host). The frass from below wasps' nests often contains unusual beetle species. Ants' nests where accessible, eg under stones or logs or in rotting wood, and when composed of plant debris, may be sifted and the beetles removed. If complete removal of the nest is impractical, as it often is in the tropics, or is unwarranted on conservation grounds, alternative methods of collecting the inquilines must be used. Tufts of grass should be buried in the larger nests and removed at intervals when beetles will often be found clinging to them. Flat pieces of wood, logs or large stones may be placed on the sides of large nests and their undersides inspected regularly. Bird and mammal nests may be treated as described for vegetable debris and broken up over a polythene sheet. Dried bird and bat dung may be broken up and sieved and all kinds of debris associated with man and domestic animals, such as bedding, stable straw, etc should be treated in a similar manner. (Care should be exercised in the use of aspirators. See p. 17). Stored food-stuffs and other dried and stored commercial materials, such as bones, hides, skins and carpets, may yield beetles if sifted or beaten. Stored agricultural produce, grain, hay-stacks, potatoes, especially if old or rotting, have a beetle fauna which is well worth investigating.

A number of beetles are associated with the bark of trees either on the outer surface, where cryptically marked species may be taken, or under the bark of healthy as well as dead and rotting trees. The surface-living species may be collected individually by diligently searching the crevices in the bark or the surface may be swept with a long-bristled broom, the beetles being collected on a beating tray or sheet placed around the bole.

Removal of the bark from living trees, using a heavy bladed knife, chisel or special bark lifters, should be done carefully and in moderation. Species making up the subcortical fauna vary accord-

144

ing to the species and the condition of the tree. Dying and freshly felled trees often carry a large and varied fauna while long dead trees that are either bone dry or completely waterlogged have far fewer associated species. Sap fluxes on woody plants are attractive to most insects including beetles. If an area is to be worked for a number of days it is often possible to wound a number of suitable trees in an area and visit them at intervals until they dry and heal. Many of the beetles that are habitually sap feeders may be attracted to baits of the more fleshy vegetables eg, potatoes, turnips, swedes etc. Compost heaps, with vegetable refuse added, may be constructed with a view to attracting sap-feeders as well as other species.

Aquatic Coleoptera

The freshwater environment is particularly rich in beetle species. Collecting the truly aquatic species requires the use of a water net or dredge. The modified form of water net as described by W A F Balfour-Browne (1940: pp 95–98) is particularly useful for gravel-beds in rivers and streams as the leading edge of the bag around the mouth of the net is protected from wear by a projecting metal rim. The technique for wielding a water net depends very largely upon the habitat and the species present. As water beetles generally keep to the shallower areas of lakes and rivers it is rarely necessary to employ a deep water dredge. The majority of species either swim freely or live on aquatic plants or under stones. In lakes and ponds, and slowly-flowing streams and rivers, there is usually no difficulty in collecting material with a water net. Stones and aquatic plants may be removed and searched for beetles in a white enamel dish containing a little water. As some of the water beetles, such as *Sphaerium*, are among the smallest insects known they are easily overlooked. For those species that live within mud or on the bottom, it is usually necessary to collect through a suitable grade of sieve.

Swiftly moving water presents quite different problems; smaller species may be swept away and lost during attempts to remove them from weed or stones. In torrent streams many species are well adapted for clinging to the stream bed. In such cases a wide mouthed net or mesh screen should be held, or secured, downstream (see p. 67) so that specimens carried away are held. When a screen is used the stream bed, and any rocks present, may be worked with a net, any gravel present disturbed with the net handle, or the bed scoured with a brush of twigs to free tightly clinging adults and larvae.

Surface-living water beetles, mainly of the family Gyrinidae, may be taken with a lighter long-handled net.

Many species inhabit that area close to the waters edge that is normally dry, but subject to periodic flooding. Trampling vegetation around a pool or stream into the water will usually force such beetles to float out and they may be picked up from the water surface with a net, brush or by hand. Splashing muddy banks with water or carefully treading them into the water will cause many beetles to emerge from their tunnels. Specimens in gravel may be collected by putting quantities of gravel into water in a suitably deep container and waiting for the non-aquatic beetles to appear and float to the surface. Waterside sand, dried mud and even damp plant debris can be subjected to the same treatment. Water beetles, especially the smaller specimens, should be collected into 80 per cent alcohol.

Traps

Unbaited pitfall traps (see p. 36) may be used to collect ground running species and where possible should be placed in natural depressions, dry stream beds etc. Gulley traps increase the catchment area in sandy areas. Bamboo or plastic tubes of approximately 50 mm (2″) diameter are split in half longitudinally and buried in sand or soft soil until the rims are level with the surface (Fig. 34). Pitfall traps are buried at either end of the gulleys so that beetles blundering into the tubes are led into the traps. If a number of gulleys are laid end to end or at right angles to one another, beetles wandering over a very large area may be shepherded into the pitfall traps. If possible, the traps should be inspected at least once a day to limit the time available for the larger carnivorous species to devour the remainder of the catch. Carrion, dung, malt, fish, cheese and sap are some of the various attractants that may be used in baited pitfall traps. The technique is similar to that used in unbaited traps although greater precautions may be needed to exclude larger animals attracted to the bait. Cheese bait is particularly attractive to cavernicolous carabids.

Window-traps This trap is designed to capture flying Coleoptera. A large sheet of clear glass or polythene is mounted in a supporting frame above a collecting trough (fig. 35), the latter may be of metal or suitable alternative. The trough is filled with water, and a few drops of detergent are added as a wetting agent. Beetles in flight hit the transparent 'window' and fall into the trough where they drown. Beetles generally fly most actively under warm and humid conditions, and consequently both this trap, the light and Malaise traps produce larger and more varied catches in the tropics.

Flying beetles usually drop to the ground when an obstacle is encountered and the window trap takes advantage of this behaviour. For this same reason the Malaise trap is generally unsuccessful as a means of collecting beetles. Upon hitting the trap the majority of beetles fall to the ground and are lost, only a small minority climb up the fabric of the trap into the killing chamber. Species that fly at dusk may not be attracted to light and these should be taken with a hand-net. 'Sweeping' the air over and around vegetation is probably the most successful method.

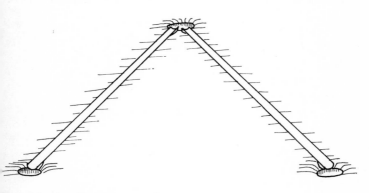

FIG. 34.   A gulley trap.

Light-traps Light trapping, as mentioned above, is most successful in the tropics where a far greater variety of species are habitaul nocturnal fliers. On suitable nights the numbers of the larger Scarabs and Dytiscids may be such as to damage the light source unless a wire gauze screen is used to protect it.

Colour Trays

Although generally used for collecting aphids, the colour trays (see p. 36) may also be successfully employed to capture beetles. Bright yellow trays are most successful and many groups of beetles, particularly Staphylinidae and many flower frequenting species, may be taken.

Beetle larvae

These may be found in as wide a range of habitats as the adults, and may be collected by many of the methods suggested for the adult stages with the exception, of course, of those methods relying on flight. Wherever possible, when a number of specimens are available, attempts should be made to rear some of the larvae through to the adult stage. Rearing the larvae is not particularly difficult in the case of plant feeders, aquatic larvae and terrestrial carnivorous species but many of the parasitic, or wood and bark-boring beetles present problems. Further information on this topic and much useful information on all aspects of collecting Coleoptera may be

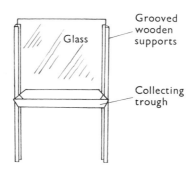

Fig. 35. A window trap.

obtained from *A Coleopterist's Handbook* published by the Amateur
Entomologists' Society in 1954.

Preserving

All beetle larvae should be collected in 80 per cent alcohol.

Adults of small species may be collected into 80 per cent alcohol in
small glass tubes which may be stored for transport in suitable glass
or plastic bottles, (see p. 60).

All adult Coleoptera, of whatever size, may be preserved dry
between layers of cellulose wadding if space is available, although
the very large specimens should not be packed together in numbers
because of the volume of their body contents and the danger of
fungal attack. The larger specimens are probably better pinned
with a large continental pin (no. 4 or 5) through the right elytron,
and stored in cork lined wooden boxes. Bracing pins inserted
along the sides of the thorax and abdomen will prevent the larger
specimens from swinging upon their pins.

STREPSIPTERA

Stylops

See Fig. 36

A small order of about 300 species of minute endoparasitic insects,
most closely related to the Coleoptera. Adult males are of a very
characteristic form and possess only one pair of developed wings,
the metathoracic pair (cf. Diptera). The larvae, and the majority
of females, are found within the body cavities of Aculeate Hymenoptera, Hemiptera, Orthoptera, Diptera and Thysanura, although
most commonly in members of the first two orders. Although a
wide variety of insects are parasitised, species of certain genera are
more liable to attack than others, eg *Andrena* (Hymenoptera) and
many Delphacid leaf-hoppers (Hemiptera). The two sexes of the
species of the family Myrmecolacidae show different host preferences,
males parasitise ants, and females Orthopteroids.

Stylops larvae pupate within the larval skin, in the host's body, but
with the fore parts extruded. Adult females are larviform and

remain in the host after pupation, except for species of Mengeidae in which the larviform females are free-living.

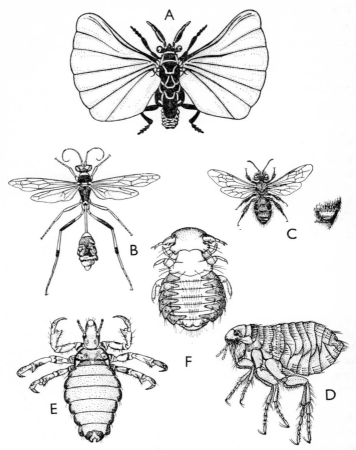

FIG. 36. Examples of the Orders: (A–C), Strepsiptera, A, a male *Stylops*, ×5½; B, a stylopised mud-dauber wasp, ×1; C, a stylopised bee, ×1. D, Siphonaptera – a flea, ×10; E, Anoplura – a pig-louse, ×8; F, Mallophaga – a peacock-louse, ×8½.

The larvae may be taken from parasitised hosts; the adult stage may be obtained by collecting the host species and keeping them alive until males emerge or mature larviform females develop. A single host may carry as many as 15 parasites. When collecting it is helpful to note that the 'stylopised' hosts often show external manifestations of their parasitised condition (see Fig. 36).

All stages should be killed and preserved in 80 per cent alcohol.

INSECTS ECTOPARASITIC ON MAMMALS AND BIRDS

Phthiraptera (Mallophaga and Anoplura), Siphonaptera, Dermaptera (part), Diptera (part), Hemiptera (part)

Representatives of all these groups are dealt with under this heading.

The techniques applied to the collecting of the insect groups parasitic externally upon mammals and birds are sufficiently similar to enable them to be considered together. Of the three main ectoparasitic groups of insects, the lice (Phthiraptera) the fleas (Siphonaptera) and the louse flies (Hippoboscidae) are found both on mammals and birds. The Mallophaga, commonly called biting or bird lice, feed on feather-parts, scales and other epidermal tissues; some species especially those on mammals, also take blood and tissue fluids. The sucking-lice (Anoplura) are exclusively parasites of mammals and as their common name suggests are adapted to suck blood. Insects from three predominantly non-parasitic orders are found as ectoparasites of mammals and birds.

Families Arixeniidae and Hemimeridae (Dermaptera) are apparently ectoparasitic on species of the bat genus *Cheiromeles* and the rat genus *Cricetomys* respectively. Bugs of the families Cimicidae are blood sucking ectoparasites of birds and mammals, while members of the family Polyctenidae are all parasites of tropical bats. Diptera of the family Hippoboscidae are found on both birds and mammals from which they take blood; Nycteribiidae are confined to bats.

Capture of the host This, of course, is the first requisite in collecting parasites. The techniques used vary considerably depending upon the primary purpose of the collector, whether it is to provide

151

museum specimens, for bird and mammal ringing, or killing for food or sport. Collecting by killing the host, although greatly simplifying the process of parasite extraction, is in most cases neither possible nor desirable. The methods used to collect the bird and mammal hosts cannot be considered here; the collector should consult Hollom & Brownlow (1955) and Southern (1964).

Collecting from living birds Some parasites are sufficiently large and active to be easily seen on the host and picked off with forceps, eg. Cimicids and Hippoboscids. Blowing through the feathers so that they are lifted will expose many more. Fleas and lice are best removed from small birds with a Fair Isle apparatus (Williamson 1954) or a simple modified version of the same (see fig. 37). The bird's head is passed through the slit of appropriate size in the oiled skin and held by the neck with the operator's fingers supporting the head, the body of the bird being suspended within the cardboard cylinder. Chloroform vapour is blown into the cylinder, the bird remaining in position for at least two minutes and,

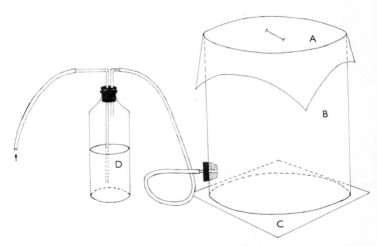

Fig. 37. Modified Fair Isle apparatus for collecting ectoparasites from living birds. A, Oiled silk with hole for bird's head; B, Cardboard cylinder; C, White tile; D, Bottle of chloroform.

if possible, induced to flap its wings occasionally. The slit in the silk rarely makes a tight collar around the neck and care should be taken that the bird is not affected by escaping vapour. If the bird blinks its eyes rapidly it should be removed from the apparatus. On removing the bird, the feathers should be ruffled over a white surface. Dead and comatose parasites from inside the apparatus may be picked up with a needle dipped in alcohol.

An alternative method of collecting feather lice is by the use of dusting powders. Suitable powders, however, are difficult to obtain in this country and many of those in use are toxic to birds and their use is not recommended.

NB In all cases, apparatus, bags and other containers in which host animals are carried should be scrupulously cleaned after use to avoid any possible confusion due to mixing of parasites from different hosts. For the same reason birds and mammals must always be carried singly in bags and after use the latter inspected for stray parasites, particular attention being paid to the corners and seams. Where there is any possibility of contamination of one host by parasites from another it is preferable to reject the specimens rather than produce data that may be erroneous. This is particularly the case with the smaller lice; fleas and the larger more active parasites eg Hippoboscids, may be kept, but notes made of the possibility of suspect data, and attached to the specimens.

Collecting from living mammals These cannot be treated with the Fair Isle apparatus as used for birds due to the general weakness of the mammalian neck. Most small mammals are also susceptible to the majority of dusting powders used on birds and these should not be used. This only leaves the manual technique of ruffling the mammal's fur by hand, or by blowing and picking the parasites from the fur with forceps, brush or needle.

NB Care should be taken to protect the hands from bites by wearing stout leather gauntlets. Many mammals, eg bats, may harbour rabies without developing the symptoms and immediate medical treatment should be obtained if the collector is bitten.

Collecting from dead birds and mammals As soon as possible after death the corpse, if of convenient size, should be placed

153

into a cotton bag, the mouth of which is securely tied to prevent the escape of louse-flies and fleas. The cotton bag is placed inside a large polythene bag or airtight box containing a wad of cotton wool soaked in chloroform. After half an hour the dead bird or mammal, and the containing bag, may be inspected for parasites. It is possible to carry out a far more thorough search in this situation and the dead host should be searched for a variety of more obscure and cryptic parasites. The quills of the wing feathers should be examined for small holes which denote the presence of lice or mites within. The head region of birds and the extremities of mammals should be inspected for stick-tight and chigger fleas both of which bear little resemblance to the usual form. It is worth bearing in mind that the majority of birds and mammals harbour ectoparasitic insects and every likely place is worth investigating, including pouches, creases, wing-folds, the vent, anal and ear regions, even the tight fur and orifices of aquatic marine mammals.

Powdering of both bird and mammal hosts is much simplified when they are dead and as a final resort, when the pelt or skin is not to be preserved, feathers and fur may be removed and dissolved. The resulting liquid is strained through a stainless steel wire gauze. Further information from Hopkins 1949, Cook 1954. This latter method should only be used where quantitative results are required, specimens so obtained are rarely of use to the taxonomist. Washing the pelts in a weak detergent solution will usually remove large numbers of parasites.

Many ectoparasites, particularly fleas, are most easily collected from the host nest or roosting site. Old nests of birds and mammals and frass from bat roosts should be placed in large polythene bags and kept until parasites hatch. The nests may also be broken up over a polythene sheet when the insects may be taken individually. **A normal aspirator should NOT be used for collecting among nest and roost material due to danger from disease.** A rubber bulb attachment or a blow-pooter should be substituted. (See p. 17). The principal causative organism is *Histoplasma capsulatum*, associated in nature with soils contaminated with bird and bat excrement and histoplasmosis has occurred in man after exposure

154

in caves, chickenhouses and cellars. (*W. H. O. Chron.* 1970). All parasitic insects are best preserved in 80 per cent alcohol in small glass tubes. Data should be full and include date of capture of host, locality and collector. Host data, species (ref. number if in doubt), age, sex, position on host and ring number of host, if the latter is a marked specimen, are particularly important. The correct identification of the host is imperative when collecting Phthiraptera and if accurate identification of the host cannot be made in the field, it should be carefully preserved in the manner suitable for the group (see Museum Handbooks Nos 1 & 2A).

Formalin should never be used for preserving ectoparasites nor cotton wool used for stoppering the tubes.

LITERATURE

Amateur Entomologist's Society, London, Collector's leaflets.

BALFOUR-BROWN, W A F 1925. *Concerning the habits of Insects.* 169 pp. Cambridge University Press.

BALFOUR-BROWN, W A F 1940. *British water beetles.* 375 pp. Ray Society, London.

BARNES, H F 1941. Sampling for leatherjackets with orthodichlorobenzene emulsion. *Ann. appl. Biol.* **28** : 23–28.

BELLAMY, R E & REEVES, W C 1952. A portable mosquito bait trap. *Mosq. News.* **12** : 256–258.

BIERNE, B P 1955. Collecting preparing and preserving insects. *Science Service Entomology Division, Canada Department of Agriculture.* Pubn 932, 133 pp. Ottawa.

BRINDLE, A 1963. Terrestrial Diptera larvae. *Entomologist's Rec. J. Var.* **75** : 47–62.

BUTLER, G D 1965. A modified Malaise insect trap. *Pan.-Pacif. Ent.* **41** (1) : 51–53.

CANTRALL, I J 1941. Notes on collecting and preserving Orthoptera. Compendium of entomological methods, pt. II. New York (Ward's Nat. Sci. Est. Inc.)

COOK, E F 1954. A modification of Hopkin's technique for collecting ectoparasites from mammal skins. *Ent. News* **15** : 35–37.

COOPER, B A (ed.). 1969 [1943]. Hymenopterists' Handbook [fascimile reprint]. *Amat. Ent.* **7**. 160 pp. London.

DETHIER, V G 1955. Mode of action of sugar-baited fly traps. *J. econ. ent.* **48** : 235–239.

FALLIS, A M & SMITH, S M 1964. Ether extracts from birds and CO_2 as attractants for some ornithophilic simuliids. *Canad. J. Zool.* **42** : 723–730.

FROST, S W 1964. Killing agents and containers for use with insect light traps. *Ent. News* **75** : 163–166.

GRESSITT, J L & GRESSITT, M K   1962.   An improved Malaise trap. *Pacif. Ins.* **4** (1) : 87–90.

HAMMOND, H E   1960.   The preservation of lepidopterous larvae using the inflation and heat-drying technique.   *J. Lepid. Soc.* **14** : 67–78.

HARRIS, R H   1964.   Vacuum dehydration and freeze drying of entire biological specimens.   *Ann. Mag. nat. hist.* (13) **7** : 65–74.

HARRISON, C J O & COWLES, G S   1970.   Birds.   Instructions for collectors.   No. 2A.   48 pp.   British Museum (Natural History), London.

HEATHCOTE, G D, PALMER, J M P & TAYLOR, L R   1969.   Sampling for aphids by traps and by crop inspection.   *Ann. appl. Biol.* **63** : 155–166.

HERTING, B   1969.   Tent window traps used for collecting Tachinids (Dipt.) at Delemont, Switzerland.   *C.I.B.C. Tech. Bull.* **12** : 1–19.

HOLLOM, P A D & BROWNLOW, H G   1955.   Trapping methods for bird ringers.   Revised ed.   B.T.O. Field Guide No. 1.   40 pp.

HOPKINS, G   1949.   The host associations of the lice of mammals. *Proc. zool. Soc. Lond.* **119** : 387–604.

HUBBELL, T H   1956.   A new collecting method: the oatmeal trail. *Ent. News* **67** : 49–51.

HUNGERFORD, H B, SPANGLER, P J & WALKER, N A   1955.   Subaquatic light traps for insects and other animal organisms.   *Trans. Kans. Acad. Sci.* **58** : 387–407.

HURD, P D   1954.   Myiasis resulting from the use of the aspirator method in the collection of insects.   *Science* **119** : 814–815.

JOHNSON, C G & TAYLOR, L R   1955.   Development of large suction traps for airborne insects.   *Ann. App. Biol.* **43** : 51–62.

KALMUS, H   1948.   Simple experiments with insects.   132 pp.   London.

KROMBEIN, K   1967.   Trap-nesting wasps and bees.   pp. vi + 570, 29 pls.   Smithsonian Press, Washington, D.C.

LEE, D J & WOODHILL, A R   1944.   Some new records and a new synonymy of Australian species of *Anopheles* (Dipt., Culicidae).   *Proc. Linn. Soc. N.S.W.* **69** : 67–72.

LEECH, H B   1955.   Cheesecloth flight trap for insects.   *Can. Ent.* **87** : 200.

MALAISE, R   1937.   A new insect-trap.   *Ent. Tidskr.* **58** : 148–160.

MARSTON, N   1965.   Recent modifications in the design of Malaise insect traps with a summary of the insects represented in collections.   *J. Kans. ent. Soc.* **38** : 154–162.

MORELAND, C R   1955.   A wind frame for trapping insects in flight. *J. econ. Ent.* **47** : 944.

MORRIS, K R S 1961. Effectiveness of traps in tsetse surveys in the Liberian rain forest. *Amer. J. trop Med. hyg.* **10** : 905–913.

MUNDIE, J H 1956. Emergence traps for squatic insects. *Mitt. int. Verein. theor. angew. Limnol.* **7.** 13 pp.

OLDROYD, H 1970. Collecting, preserving and studying insects. 2nd edn. 366 pp. London.

OLDROYD, H 1972. Insects and their world. 2nd edn. British Museum (Natural History), London.

OMAN, P W & CUSHMAN, A D 1948. Collection and preservation of insects. U.S. Dept. Agriculture Misc. Pub. No. **601.** 42 pp. Washington, D.C.

RENNISON, B D & ROBERTSON, D H H 1959. The use of carbon dioxide as an attractant for catching tsetse. *Rep. E. Afr. Trypan. Res. Organ.* **1958** : 26.

RICHARDS, O W & RICHARDS, M J 1951. Observations on the social wasps of South America (Hymenoptera Vespidae). *Trans. R. ent. Soc. Lond.* **102** : 1–170.

ROBINSON, H S & ROBINSON, P J M 1950. Some notes on the observed behaviour of Lepidoptera in flight in the vicinity of light-sources together with a description of a light-trap designed to take entomological samples. *Ent. Gaz.* **1** : 3–15.

RYDON, A 1964. Notes on the use of butterfly traps in East Africa. *J. Lep. Soc.* **18** : 51–58.

SALMON, J T 1946. A portable apparatus for the extraction from leaf mould of Collembola and other minute organisms. *Dom. Mus. Rec. Ent.* **1** : 13–18.

SOUTHERN, H N (ed.) 1964. The handbook of British Mammals. xxi + 465 pp. Oxford.

SOUTHWOOD, T R E 1966. Ecological methods. 391 pp. London.

STANDFAST, H A 1965. A miniature light trap which automatically segregates the catch into hourly samples. *Mosq. News.* **25** : 48–53.

TAYLOR, L R 1962. The absolute efficiency of insect suction traps. *Ann. appl. Biol.* **50** : 405–421.

THORSTEINSON, A J, BRACKEN, G K & HANEC, W 1965. The orientation behaviour of horse flies and deer flies (Tabanidae, Diptera). III. The use of traps in the study of orientation of Tabanids in the field. *Ent. exp. appl.* **8** : 189–192.

TOWNES, H 1962. Design for a Malaise trap. *Proc. ent. Soc. Wash.* **64** : 162–253.

TROUGHT, T (ed.) 1951. Practical methods and hints for Lepidopterists. *Amat. Ent.* **9.** 42 pp. London.

WALSH, G B & DIBB, J R (eds) 1954. A Coleopterist's Handbook. *Amat. Ent.* **11**. 120 pp. London.

WILLIAMS, C B 1951. Comparing the efficiency of insect traps. *Bull. Ent. Res.* **42** : 513–517.

WILLIAMSON, K 1954. The Fair Isle apparatus for collecting bird ecto-parasites. *Brit. Birds* **47** : 234–5.

W.H.O. Chron. **24** : 512–515. Mycoses in the Americas.

APPENDIX

Berlese Mountant

May be obtained from Searle Diagnostic,
Lane End Road,
High Wycombe.

B. M. Mixture

Make a saturated solution of naphthalene in S.B.P. 4. lighter fuel, a small quantity of Beechwood creosote may be added if desired (up to c. 15 per cent.).

Chlorocresol

This substance may be used to retain fresh specimens in a relaxed condition for long periods.   A layer of the chlorocresol crystals is placed in the bottom of an airtight tin or plastic box, the freshly-killed insects are added in layers of Cellosene or in papers.   The tin is sealed when full.

The presence of a few large, fleshy insects helps to keep up the moisture content of smaller ones.

This method has been largely used by the museum staff collecting Coleoptera and has also been successfully used with butterflies in East Africa.

Corbett and Pendlebury's mixture

Powdered naphthalene   6 parts
Chloroform   1 part
Beechwood creosote   1 part
Petrol   4 parts
Mix as follows:

$1\frac{1}{2}$ parts naphthalene to 1 part chloroform, add $1\frac{1}{2}$ parts naphthalene and 1 part Beechwood creosote, stir well. Then add remaining 3 parts naphthalene and the petrol to increase the bulk.

Store in airtight bottle and stir well before and during use

'Dust-shot' cartridge

Made by Ely Cartridge Division (part of Imperial Metal Industries). Will fit 0·22 gauge gun, usually a rifle or else spread is too great. Referred to as no. 12 shot. Can be fired from smooth or rifled barrel. Brass-cased. Cost [Feb. 1972]: £8·25 per 1000.

Embalming fluid

Formula

Mix

60 ml	Toluene or xylene
25 ml	Tert- butyl alcohol
15 ml	Ethyl alcohol
5 g	Phenol
20 g	p-dichlorbenzene
10 drops	Canada Balsam in xylene

Method

The fluid is to be injected into the body cavity of the insect. This causes the specimen to dry rapidly and retain most of its colour. Enter the syringe between tergites in the anal region and push up into head, withdraw syringe gradually while injecting.

Formaldehyde buffers

Buffers for formaldehyde Buffers are normally used in physiological experiments so that experimental tissues are bathed in them and the pH is not greatly affected. For the neutralisation of formaldehyde hexamine is used. 100 grammes per litre neat formaldehyde generally affords neutrality but this should be checked with a meter because batches of hexamine vary. Sodium carbonate and/or calcium carbonate may be used in the same way.

Neutral formaldehyde may also be obtained as follows: 10 ml formaldehyde is diluted with 90 ml distilled water. Neutralise by adding 0·35 g sodium dihydrogen phosphate (anhydrous) and 0·65 g disodium hydrogen phosphate per 100 ml diluted formalin.

Pampel's fluid

Original		*Improved*	
Formalin 40%	6 parts	Formalin 35%	6 parts
Ethyl alcohol 95%	15 parts	Ethyl alcohol 95%	15 parts
Glacial acetic acid	4 parts	Glacial acetic acid	2 parts
Aqua dist.	30 parts	Aqua dist.	30 parts

Mix and use cold.

For killing and fixing larvae etc, preserves the colour and texture. Immerse in fluid while alive and leave to harden for up to 2–3 weeks, then remove and store in 80 per cent alcohol.

Picro-chlor acetic: fixative

All parts by volume

1% sol picric acid in 96% alcohol	12 parts
Chloroform	2 parts
Glacial acetic acid	1 part

Put insects in alive and leave 12 hours, rinse in several changes of 70 per cent alcohol and store in 70 per cent alcohol. Stains material and storage fluid yellow.

Tacky-tack

Craven Chemicals, Evesham

Formula

Mix

80 parts	Castor oil 1st pressing	Joseph Gilman & Son
15 parts	Manilla gum copal	George Hull Ltd
16½ parts	American colophony resin	Philip Harris
4 parts	Carnuba wax	Philip Harris
2½ parts	Japan wax	Philip Harris
1 part	Orange cerasine wax	Joseph Gilman & Son
2 parts	Light ozyokerite wax	,,

Method

Take 60 parts of castor oil and 15 parts of gum copal. Heat strongly until melted into one homogeneous liquor. Add the colophony resin and heat until melted. Add carnuba and melt,

Japan and melt, then ozyokerite and cerasine and melt, and finally add the remaining 20 parts of castor oil.

For higher quality increase the gum copal to 30 parts, the carnuba to 6½ and reduce the Japan wax to 1.

Suppliers

Joseph Gilman & Son	Shadwell House
	Lower Loveday Street
	Birmingham 4
George Hull Ltd,	28 Horsefair
	Birmingham 1
Philip Harris Medical Ltd,	Hazelwell Lane
	Stirchley
	Birmingham 30

Yellow formalin compound

Yellow formalin compound or formaldehyde releaser 'Dowicil 100 R'. This yellow powder is made up into a 10 per cent aqueous solution just prior to preservation. Immersion of insects in this solution will cause formaldehyde to be liberated by the presence of protein. Prepared by the Dow Chemical Company.

INDEX

164

167